50 CHALLENGING CALCULUS PROBLEMS

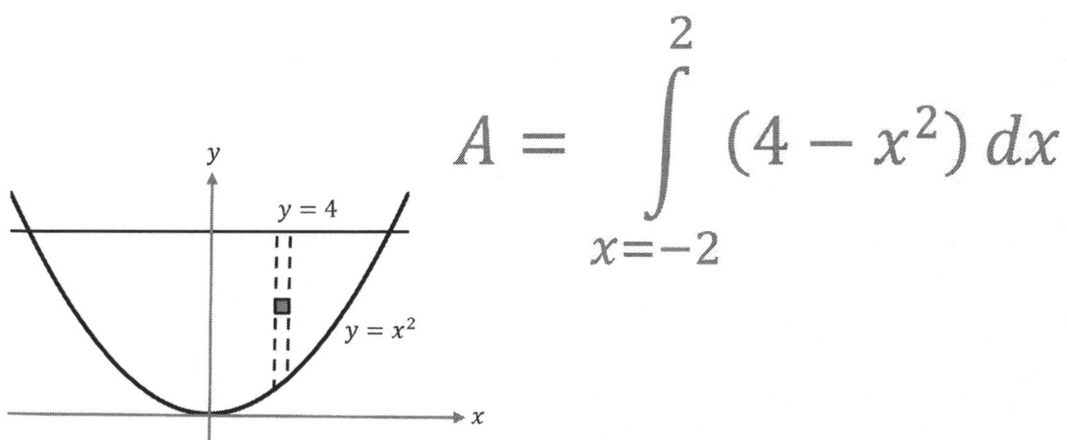

FULLY SOLVED

Chris McMullen, Ph.D.

50 Challenging Calculus Problems (Fully Solved)
Improve Your Math Fluency
Chris McMullen, Ph.D.

www.monkeyphysicsblog.wordpress.com
www.improveyourmathfluency.com
www.chrismcmullen.wordpress.com

Zishka Publishing
ISBN: 978-1-941691-26-7

Textbooks > Math > Calculus
Study Guides > Workbooks> Math
Education > Math > Calculus

Date: ______________ Name: ______________________________

Problem 1

Directions: Perform the following derivative, where $\cot(4\theta^2 - 1) > 0$.

$$\frac{d}{d\theta}\ln[\cot(4\theta^2 - 1)]$$

❖You can find the solution on the following page.

Solution to Problem 1

This is an application of the chain rule, involving inside and outside functions. After you take a derivative of the outside function, you then take a derivative of the inside function.

- The outside function, $f(u)$, is a natural logarithm: $f(u) = \ln u$.
- The inside function, $u(\theta)$, is a cotangent: $u(\theta) = \cot(4\theta^2 - 1)$.

According to the chain rule, we multiply the two derivatives together:

$$\frac{df}{d\theta} = \frac{df}{du}\frac{du}{d\theta} = \left[\frac{d}{du}\ln u\right]\left[\frac{d}{d\theta}\cot(4\theta^2 - 1)\right]$$

The derivative of the natural logarithm is $\frac{d}{du}\ln u = \frac{1}{u}$:

$$\frac{df}{d\theta} = \frac{1}{u}\frac{d}{d\theta}\cot(4\theta^2 - 1) = \frac{1}{\cot(4\theta^2 - 1)}\frac{d}{d\theta}\cot(4\theta^2 - 1)$$

To take the derivative of the cotangent function, we will apply the chain rule again:

- The outside function, $g(v)$, is a cotangent: $g(v) = \cot v$.
- The inside function, $v(\theta)$, is a polynomial: $v(\theta) = 4\theta^2 - 1$.

Apply the chain rule again:

$$\frac{df}{d\theta} = \frac{1}{\cot(4\theta^2 - 1)}\frac{d}{d\theta}\cot(4\theta^2 - 1) = \frac{1}{\cot(4\theta^2 - 1)}\frac{dg}{dv}\frac{dv}{d\theta}$$

$$= \frac{1}{\cot(4\theta^2 - 1)}\left[\frac{d}{dv}\cot v\right]\left[\frac{d}{d\theta}(4\theta^2 - 1)\right]$$

The derivatives are $\frac{d}{dv}\cot v = -\csc^2 v$ and $\frac{d}{d\theta}(4\theta^2 - 1) = 8\theta$.

$$\frac{df}{d\theta} = \frac{1}{\cot(4\theta^2 - 1)}[-\csc^2 v][8\theta] = -\frac{8\theta\csc^2 v}{\cot(4\theta^2 - 1)} = \boxed{-\frac{8\theta\csc^2(4\theta^2 - 1)}{\cot(4\theta^2 - 1)}}$$

Recall that $\csc v = \frac{1}{\sin v}$ and $\cot v = \frac{\cos v}{\sin v}$. Thus, an alternative form of the answer is:

$$\frac{df}{d\theta} = -(8\theta)[\csc^2(4\theta^2 - 1)]\left[\frac{1}{\cot(4\theta^2 - 1)}\right] = -(8\theta)\left[\frac{1}{\sin^2(4\theta^2 - 1)}\right]\left[\frac{\sin(4\theta^2 - 1)}{\cos(4\theta^2 - 1)}\right]$$

$$= \boxed{-\frac{8\theta}{\sin(4\theta^2 - 1)\cos(4\theta^2 - 1)}} = \boxed{-8\theta\csc(4\theta^2 - 1)\sec(4\theta^2 - 1)}$$

If you apply the trig identity $\sin x \cos x = \frac{\sin 2x}{2}$, you can also express the answer as:

$$\frac{df}{d\theta} = -\frac{8\theta}{[\sin(8\theta^2 - 2)]/2} = \boxed{-\frac{16\theta}{\sin(8\theta^2 - 2)}} = \boxed{-16\theta\csc(8\theta^2 - 2)}$$

Date: ____________ Name: ______________________________

Problem 2

Directions: Perform the following integral as instructed in each part below.

$$\int (2 - 3x)^2 \, dx$$

(A) Multiply $2 - 3x$ by itself and integrate each term separately.

(B) Integrate using the method of substitution with $u = 2 - 3x$.

(C) Compare your answers for parts (A) and (B). Explain any differences.

❖You can find the solution on the following page.

Solution to Problem 2

(A) First multiply $2 - 3x$ by itself:

$$(2-3x)^2 = (2-3x)(2-3x) = 4 - 6x - 6x + 9x^2$$

$$(2-3x)^2 = 4 - 12x + 9x^2$$

Substitute this into the integral:

$$\int (2-3x)^2\,dx = \int (4 - 12x + 9x^2)\,dx$$

Integrate term by term according to $\int (y_1 + y_2 + y_3)\,dx = \int y_1\,dx + \int y_2\,dx + \int y_3\,dx$.

$$= \int 4\,dx - \int 12x\,dx + \int 9x^2\,dx$$

$$= 4x - 6x^2 + 3x^3 + c = \boxed{3x^3 - 6x^2 + 4x + c}$$

As with all indefinite integrals, there is an arbitrary constant of integration, c.

(B) Implicitly differentiate $u = 2 - 3x$ to get $du = -3\,dx$. (A derivative of $2 - 3x$ with respect to x equals -3.) Divide both sides of the equation $du = -3\,dx$ by -3 to get $-\frac{du}{3} = dx$. Substitute $u = 2 - 3x$ and $dx = -\frac{du}{3}$ into the integral.

$$\int (2-3x)^2\,dx = \int u^2\left(-\frac{dx}{3}\right) = -\frac{1}{3}\int u^2\,du = -\frac{1}{3}\left(\frac{u^3}{3}\right) + c = -\frac{u^3}{9} + c$$

$$= -\frac{(2-3x)^3}{9} + c = -\frac{(2-3x)^2(2-3x)}{9} + c$$

$$= -\frac{(4 - 12x + 9x^2)(2-3x)}{9} + c$$

$$= -\frac{8 - 12x - 24x + 36x^2 + 18x^2 - 27x^3}{9} + c$$

$$= -\frac{8 - 36x + 54x^2 - 27x^3}{9} + c$$

$$= -\frac{8}{9} - \left(-\frac{36x}{9}\right) - \frac{54x^2}{9} - \left(-\frac{27x^3}{9}\right) + c$$

$$= -\frac{8}{9} + 4x - 6x^2 + 3x^3 + c = \boxed{3x^3 - 6x^2 + 4x - \frac{8}{9} + c}$$

(C) At first, it may appear that $3x^3 - 6x^2 + 4x + c$ and $3x^3 - 6x^2 + 4x - \frac{8}{9} + c$ differ by $\frac{8}{9}$. However, $\frac{8}{9}$ is just a constant. In part (B), we could write $3x^3 - 6x^2 + 4x + c$ instead of $3x^3 - 6x^2 + 4x - \frac{8}{9} + c$ by lumping the term $-\frac{8}{9}$ with the constant c.

Date: ____________ Name: ____________________________

Problem 3

Directions: Perform the following eighth derivative.

$$\frac{d^8}{dx^8}\left(\frac{x^{10}}{10!} - \frac{x^9}{9!} + \frac{x^8}{8!} - \frac{x^7}{7!}\right)$$

Note that $n!$ (read as n factorial) means $n! = n(n-1)(n-2)\cdots(3)(2)(1)$, meaning to multiply n by all of the integers less than n until you reach the number 1. The eighth derivative is similar to a second derivative, except that it involves taking additional derivatives.

❖ You can find the solution on the following page.

Solution to Problem 3

We need to take eight consecutive derivatives of the given polynomial. It may help to work out the first few derivatives:

$$\frac{d}{dx}\left(\frac{x^{10}}{10!}-\frac{x^9}{9!}+\frac{x^8}{8!}-\frac{x^7}{7!}\right)=\frac{10x^9}{10!}-\frac{9x^8}{9!}+\frac{8x^7}{8!}-\frac{7x^6}{7!}=\frac{x^9}{9!}-\frac{x^8}{8!}+\frac{x^7}{7!}-\frac{x^6}{6!}$$

$$\frac{d^2}{dx^2}\left(\frac{x^{10}}{10!}-\frac{x^9}{9!}+\frac{x^8}{8!}-\frac{x^7}{7!}\right)=\frac{d}{dx}\left(\frac{x^9}{9!}-\frac{x^8}{8!}+\frac{x^7}{7!}-\frac{x^6}{6!}\right)=\frac{x^8}{8!}-\frac{x^7}{7!}+\frac{x^6}{6!}-\frac{x^5}{5!}$$

$$\frac{d^3}{dx^3}\left(\frac{x^{10}}{10!}-\frac{x^9}{9!}+\frac{x^8}{8!}-\frac{x^7}{7!}\right)=\frac{d}{dx}\left(\frac{x^8}{8!}-\frac{x^7}{7!}+\frac{x^6}{6!}-\frac{x^5}{5!}\right)=\frac{x^7}{7!}-\frac{x^6}{6!}+\frac{x^5}{5!}-\frac{x^4}{4!}$$

Note, for example, that $\frac{10x^9}{10!}=\frac{10x^9}{(10)(9!)}=\frac{x^9}{9!}$ because $10!=(10)(9!)$. What is the pattern here? After k derivatives, a term of the form $\frac{x^n}{n!}$ changes into $\frac{x^{n-k}}{(n-k)!}$. For example, in the third derivative ($k=3$), the term $\frac{x^{10}}{10!}$ (where $n=10$) changes into $\frac{x^{10-3}}{(10-3)!}=\frac{x^7}{7!}$. This problem asks for the eighth derivative, which means to set $k=8$:

$$\frac{d^8}{dx^8}\left(\frac{x^{10}}{10!}-\frac{x^9}{9!}+\frac{x^8}{8!}-\frac{x^7}{7!}\right)=\frac{x^{10-8}}{(10-8)!}-\frac{x^{9-8}}{(9-8)!}+\frac{x^{8-8}}{(8-8)!}-0$$

$$=\frac{x^2}{2!}-\frac{x^1}{1!}+\frac{x^0}{0!}=\frac{x^2}{2}-\frac{x}{1}+\frac{1}{1}=\boxed{\frac{x^2}{2}-x+1}=\boxed{\frac{x^2-2x+2}{2}}$$

Do you have questions about this? Following are some answers:

- What happened to $\frac{x^1}{1!}$? Since $x^1=x$ and $1!=1$, it follows that $\frac{x^1}{1!}=\frac{x}{1}=x$.
- What happened to $\frac{x^0}{0!}$? Since $x^0=1$ and $0!=1$, it follows that $\frac{x^0}{0!}=\frac{1}{1}=1$.
- How could you solve this problem if you didn't know that $0!=1$? That's easy: Just keep taking derivatives (or deduce the pattern using logic and reason).
- Why is the last term zero? It's because the seventh derivative of $\frac{x^7}{7!}$ equals 1, since $\frac{d^7}{dx^7}\frac{x^7}{7!}=\frac{x^{7-7}}{(7-7)!}=\frac{x^0}{0!}=\frac{1}{1}=1$. The eighth derivative is the derivative of the seventh derivative: $\frac{d^8}{dx^8}\frac{x^7}{7!}=\frac{d}{dx}\left(\frac{d^7}{dx^7}\frac{x^7}{7!}\right)=\frac{d}{dx}(1)=0$. A derivative of a constant equals zero.

Date: ______________ Name: ______________________________

Problem 4

Directions: Perform the following integral.

$$\int \frac{dx}{\sqrt{3x+4}}$$

❖You can find the solution on the following page.

Solution to Problem 4

Make the substitution $u = 3x + 4$. Implicitly differentiate $u = 3x + 4$ to get $du = 3\,dx$. (A derivative of $3x + 4$ with respect to x equals 3.) Divide both sides of the equation $du = 3\,dx$ by 3 to get $\frac{du}{3} = dx$. Substitute $u = 3x + 4$ and $dx = \frac{du}{3}$ into the integral.

$$\int \frac{dx}{\sqrt{3x+4}} = \int \frac{du}{3\sqrt{u}} = \frac{1}{3}\int \frac{du}{u^{1/2}} = \frac{1}{3}\int u^{-1/2}\,du$$

Note that $\sqrt{u} = u^{1/2}$ and that $\frac{1}{u^n} = u^{-n}$. Apply the formula $\int ax^b\,dx = \frac{ax^{b+1}}{b+1} + c$ (which is valid for $b \neq -1$) with $b = -\frac{1}{2}$.

$$\frac{1}{3}\int u^{-1/2}\,du = \frac{1}{3}\frac{u^{-1/2+1}}{-\frac{1}{2}+1} + c = \frac{1}{3}\frac{u^{1/2}}{\frac{1}{2}} + c = \frac{2}{3}u^{1/2} + c = \frac{2}{3}\sqrt{u} + c$$

$$= \boxed{\frac{2}{3}\sqrt{3x+4} + c}$$

Note that $-\frac{1}{2} + 1 = -\frac{1}{2} + \frac{2}{2} = \frac{-1+2}{2} = \frac{1}{2}$ (add or subtract fractions by finding a common denominator) and that $\frac{1}{3} \div \frac{1}{2} = \frac{1}{3} \times \frac{2}{1} = \frac{2}{3}$ (dividing by a fraction equates to multiplying by its reciprcal, and the reciprocal of $\frac{1}{2}$ is $\frac{2}{1}$). As with all indefinite integrals, there is an arbitrary constant of integration, c.

Check the answer: Take a derivative of the result with respect to x. Compare this to the original integrand. Apply the chain rule (which we also used in Solution 1) with the outside function $f = \frac{2}{3}\sqrt{u} + c$ and the inside function $u = 3x + 4$.

$$\frac{d}{dx}\left(\frac{2}{3}\sqrt{3x+4} + c\right) = \frac{df}{dx} = \frac{df}{du}\frac{du}{dx} = \frac{d}{du}\left(\frac{2}{3}\sqrt{u} + c\right)\frac{d}{dx}(3x+4)$$

$$\frac{d}{du}\left(\frac{2}{3}u^{1/2} + c\right)(3) = (3)\left(\frac{1}{2}\right)\left(\frac{2}{3}\right)u^{-1/2} = u^{-1/2} = \frac{1}{u^{1/2}} = \frac{1}{\sqrt{u}} = \frac{1}{\sqrt{3x+4}}$$

Note that $\sqrt{u} = u^{1/2}$ and that $\frac{1}{u^n} = u^{-n}$. Also note that $\frac{d}{du}u^{1/2} = \frac{1}{2}u^{-1/2}$ according to the formula $\frac{d}{dx}ax^b = bax^{b-1}$ with $b = \frac{1}{2}$.

Date: ____________________ Name: ____

Problem 5

Directions: Evaluate the following limit.

$$\lim_{x \to 0} \frac{x^4 - 3x^3 + 8x^2}{x^3 - 2x^2}$$

❖You can find the solution on the following page.

Solution to Problem 5

The limit doesn't equal zero, even though the numerator, $x^4 - 3x^3 + 8x^2$, approaches zero in the limit that x approaches zero. Why not? The denominator, $x^3 - 2x^2$, also approaches zero in the limit that x approaches zero. Recall from arithmetic that the fraction $0/0$ is indeterminate. This limit *can* be evaluated: We need to apply algebra in a way that renders the limit in a determinate form. The problem is that every term in both the numerator and denominator is proportional to a power of x. How can we apply algebra to eliminate the power of x in at least one term? The answer is to divide the numerator and denominator of the fraction each by x^2.

$$\lim_{x\to 0}\frac{x^4 - 3x^3 + 8x^2}{x^3 - 2x^2} = \lim_{x\to 0}\left(\frac{x^4 - 3x^3 + 8x^2}{x^3 - 2x^2}\right)\frac{\frac{1}{x^2}}{\frac{1}{x^2}}$$

$$= \lim_{x\to 0}\frac{(x^4 - 3x^3 + 8x^2)\frac{1}{x^2}}{(x^3 - 2x^2)\frac{1}{x^2}} = \lim_{x\to 0}\frac{\frac{x^4}{x^2} - \frac{3x^3}{x^2} + \frac{8x^2}{x^2}}{\frac{x^3}{x^2} - \frac{2x^2}{x^2}} = \lim_{x\to 0}\frac{x^2 - 3x + 8}{x - 2}$$

Now the limit can be evaluated easily:

$$\lim_{x\to 0}\frac{x^2 - 3x + 8}{x - 2} = \frac{\lim\limits_{x\to 0}(x^2 - 3x + 8)}{\lim\limits_{x\to 0}(x - 2)} = \frac{0^2 - 3(0) + 8}{0 - 2} = \frac{8}{-2} = \boxed{-4}$$

Strictly speaking, we don't "plug in" the numerical value of $x = 0$ in order to evaluate the limit. Rather, we analyze the functions $x^2 - 3x + 8$ and $x - 2$ (try graphing these functions, for example) and determine what value each function approaches as the variable x approaches zero. It should be easy to see that $x^2 - 3x + 8$ approaches 8 and that $x - 2$ approaches -2 as x approaches zero. In contrast, it wasn't as easy to see that the original fraction, $\frac{x^4-3x^3+8x^2}{x^3-2x^2}$, approaches -4 in the limit that x approaches zero (in fact, the "plugging in" approach leads to the problem of the indeterminate $0/0$). We applied a little algebra and the property of limits that $\lim\limits_{x\to c}\frac{f}{g} = \frac{\lim\limits_{x\to c} f}{\lim\limits_{x\to c} g}$ (provided that $\lim\limits_{x\to c} g \neq 0$). If you apply l'Hôpital's rule twice (because once will still be indeterminate), you similarly get $\lim\limits_{x\to 0}\frac{x^4-3x^3+8x^2}{x^3-2x^2} = \frac{\frac{d^2}{dx^2}(x^4-3x^3+8x^2)\big|_{x=0}}{\frac{d^2}{dx^2}(x^3-2x^2)\big|_{x=0}} = \frac{(12x^2-18x+16)|_{x=0}}{(6x-4)|_{x=0}} = \frac{16}{-4} = -4$. If you plug in $x = 0.1$, you can see that $\frac{0.1^4-3(0.1)^3+8(0.1)^2}{0.1^3-2(0.1)^2} = \frac{0.0771}{-0.019} = -4.06 \approx -4$.

Date: ____________ Name: ______________________________

Problem 6

Directions: Find the absolute extrema for the function below over the interval [1,10].

$$f(x) = \frac{5}{x^4} - \frac{30}{x^6}$$

❖You can find the solution on the following page.

Solution to Problem 6

Take a derivative of $f(x)$ with respect to x. Apply the rule $\frac{d}{dx}ax^b = bax^{b-1}$. Note that $\frac{1}{x^n} = x^{-n}$.

$$\frac{df}{dx} = \frac{d}{dx}\left(\frac{5}{x^4} - \frac{30}{x^6}\right) = \frac{d}{dx}(5x^{-4} - 30x^{-6}) = (-4)(5)x^{-5} - (-6)(30)x^{-7}$$

$$= -20x^{-5} + 180x^{-7} = -\frac{20}{x^5} + \frac{180}{x^7}$$

Set the first derivative equal to zero. Solve for x. Call these values x_c.

$$\frac{df}{dx} = 0 \quad \to \quad -\frac{20}{x_c^5} + \frac{180}{x_c^7} = 0 \quad \to \quad \frac{180}{x_c^7} = \frac{20}{x_c^5}$$

Multiply both sides of the equation by x_c^7. Note that $\frac{x^7}{x^5} = x^{7-5} = x^2$ since $x^{m-n} = \frac{x^m}{x^n}$.

$$180 = 20x_c^2 \quad \to \quad 9 = x_c^2 \quad \to \quad \sqrt{9} = x_c \quad \to \quad \pm 3 = x_c$$

Why $\pm$? Because $(-3)^2 = (-3)(-3) = 9$ and $3^2 = 9$ both solve the equation $9 = x_c^2$. However, only the solution $x_c = +3$ lies in the specified interval, $1 \leq x \leq 10$. Take a second derivative of $f(x)$ with respect to x:

$$\frac{d^2f}{dx^2} = \frac{d}{dx}\left(\frac{df}{dx}\right) = \frac{d}{dx}(-20x^{-5} + 180x^{-7})$$

$$= (-5)(-20)x^{-6} + (-7)(180)x^{-8} = \frac{100}{x^6} - \frac{1260}{x^8}$$

Evaluate the second derivative at $x_c = 3$ (which we found previously).

$$\left.\frac{d^2f}{dx^2}\right|_{x=3} = \frac{100}{3^6} - \frac{1260}{3^8} = \frac{100}{729} - \frac{1260}{6561} \approx -0.054869684$$

There is a relative maximum at $x_c = 3$, since the second derivative is negative there. Evaluate the function at $x_c = 3$ and the endpoints of the interval ($x = 1$ and $x = 10$).

$$f(3) = \frac{5}{3^4} - \frac{30}{3^6} = \frac{5}{81} - \frac{30}{729} = \frac{45}{729} - \frac{30}{729} = \frac{15}{729} = \frac{5}{243} \approx 0.020576132$$

$$f(1) = \frac{5}{1^4} - \frac{30}{1^6} = 5 - 30 = -25$$

$$f(10) = \frac{5}{10^4} - \frac{30}{10^6} = \frac{5}{10{,}000} - \frac{30}{1{,}000{,}000} = \frac{1}{2000} - \frac{3}{100{,}000} = 0.00047$$

Over the interval $[1,10]$, the given function has an absolute minimum value of $\boxed{-25}$ (when $x = 1$) and an absolute maximum value of $\approx \boxed{0.020576132}$ (when $x = 3$).

Date: ____________________ Name: ____

Problem 7

Directions: Perform the following derivatives, where a is a constant. Which of these derivatives is unusual compared to the others? Show and explain.

$$\frac{d}{dx}\sin(ax) \quad , \quad \frac{d}{dx}e^{ax} \quad , \quad \frac{d}{dx}\ln(ax) \quad , \quad \frac{d}{dx}\sqrt{ax}$$

❖ You can find the solution on the following page.

Solution to Problem 7

Perform each derivative and compare. Apply the chain rule (like we did in Solution 1) with inside and outside functions, using $u = ax$ for the inside function.

$$\frac{d\sin(ax)}{dx} = \frac{df}{dx} = \frac{df}{du}\frac{du}{dx} = \left(\frac{d}{du}\sin u\right)\left(\frac{d}{dx}ax\right) = (\cos u)(a) = a\cos u = a\cos(ax)$$

$$\frac{de^{ax}}{dx} = \frac{df}{dx} = \frac{df}{du}\frac{du}{dx} = \left(\frac{d}{du}e^{u}\right)\left(\frac{d}{dx}ax\right) = (e^{u})(a) = ae^{u} = ae^{ax}$$

$$\frac{d\ln(ax)}{dx} = \frac{df}{dx} = \frac{df}{du}\frac{du}{dx} = \left(\frac{d}{du}\ln u\right)\left(\frac{d}{dx}ax\right) = \left(\frac{1}{u}\right)(a) = \frac{a}{u} = \frac{a}{ax} = \frac{1}{x}$$

$$\frac{d\sqrt{ax}}{dx} = \frac{df}{dx} = \frac{df}{du}\frac{du}{dx} = \left(\frac{d}{du}\sqrt{u}\right)\left(\frac{d}{dx}ax\right) = \left(\frac{d}{du}u^{1/2}\right)(a) = a\left(\frac{1}{2}\right)u^{-1/2}$$

$$= \frac{a}{2u^{1/2}} = \frac{a}{2\sqrt{u}} = \frac{a}{2\sqrt{ax}} = \frac{a}{2\sqrt{ax}}\frac{\sqrt{ax}}{\sqrt{ax}} = \frac{a\sqrt{ax}}{2ax} = \frac{\sqrt{ax}}{2x}$$

Note that $\sqrt{u} = u^{1/2}$ and $u^{-1/2} = \frac{1}{u^{1/2}}$ according to $\frac{1}{u^n} = u^{-n}$. In the last derivative, we rationalized the denominator by multiplying $\frac{a}{\sqrt{ax}}$ by $\frac{\sqrt{ax}}{\sqrt{ax}}$. Note that $\sqrt{ax}\sqrt{ax} = ax$, just as $\sqrt{u}\sqrt{u} = \left(\sqrt{u}\right)^2 = u$. Examine the results closely:

$$\frac{d}{dx}\sin(ax) = \boxed{a\cos(ax)}$$

$$\frac{d}{dx}e^{ax} = \boxed{ae^{ax}}$$

$$\frac{d}{dx}\ln(ax) = \boxed{\frac{1}{x}}$$

$$\frac{d}{dx}\sqrt{ax} = \boxed{\frac{\sqrt{ax}}{2x}}$$

What seems unusual about one of these derivatives? The constant a canceled out in the derivative of the natural logarithm, but is present in all of the others. Why does a cancel out in the derivative of $\ln(ax)$? One way to see this is to recall the logarithmic identity $\ln(xy) = \ln x + \ln y$:

$$\frac{d}{dx}\ln(ax) = \frac{d}{dx}(\ln a + \ln x) = \frac{d}{dx}\ln a + \frac{d}{dx}\ln x = 0 + \frac{1}{x} = \frac{1}{x}$$

The first term equals zero because the derivative of a constant is zero. Note that $\ln a$ is a constant because a is a constant. Therefore, $\frac{d}{dx}\ln a = 0$.

Date: ________________ Name: ____________________________________

Problem 8

Directions: Perform the following integral.

$$\int_{\theta=0}^{\frac{\pi}{2}} \cos^{15}\theta \sin^3\theta \, d\theta$$

❖You can find the solution on the following page.

Solution to Problem 8

From the identity $\sin^2\theta + \cos^2\theta = 1$, we get $\sin^2\theta = 1 - \cos^2\theta$. Use this to rewrite $\sin^3\theta$ as $\sin^3\theta = \sin\theta\sin^2\theta = \sin\theta\,(1-\cos^2\theta)$.

$$\int_{\theta=0}^{\pi/2} \cos^{15}\theta\sin^3\theta\,d\theta = \int_{\theta=0}^{\pi/2} \cos^{15}\theta\sin\theta\,(1-\cos^2\theta)\,d\theta$$

Separate this into two integrals, applying the rule $\int(y_1+y_2)\,dx = \int y_1\,dx + \int y_2\,dx$. Note that $\cos^{15}\theta\sin\theta\,(1-\cos^2\theta) = \cos^{15}\theta\sin\theta - \cos^{17}\theta\sin\theta$.

$$\int_{\theta=0}^{\pi/2} \cos^{15}\theta\sin\theta\,(1-\cos^2\theta)\,d\theta = \int_{\theta=0}^{\pi/2} \cos^{15}\theta\sin\theta\,d\theta - \int_{\theta=0}^{\pi/2} \cos^{17}\theta\sin\theta\,d\theta$$

It is convenient to make the substitution $u = \cos\theta$. Implicitly differentiate $u = \cos\theta$ to get $du = -\sin\theta\,d\theta$. (A derivative of $\cos\theta$ with respect to θ equals $-\sin\theta$.) Multiply both sides of $du = -\sin\theta\,d\theta$ by -1 to get $-du = \sin\theta\,d\theta$. Use the equation $u = \cos\theta$ to determine the new limits of integration:

$$u(0) = \cos 0 = 1 \quad , \quad u\left(\frac{\pi}{2}\right) = \cos\left(\frac{\pi}{2}\right) = \cos 90° = 0$$

Substitute $u = \cos\theta$ and $-du = \sin\theta\,d\theta$ into the integrals.

$$\int_{\theta=0}^{\pi/2} \cos^{15}\theta\sin\theta\,d\theta - \int_{\theta=0}^{\pi/2} \cos^{17}\theta\sin\theta\,d\theta = \int_{u=1}^{0} u^{15}\,(-du) - \int_{u=1}^{0} u^{17}\,(-du)$$

$$= -\int_{u=1}^{0} u^{15}\,du + \int_{u=1}^{0} u^{17}\,du = -\left[\frac{u^{16}}{16}\right]_{u=1}^{0} + \left[\frac{u^{18}}{18}\right]_{u=1}^{0}$$

We applied the formula $\int ax^b\,dx = \frac{ax^{b+1}}{b+1} + c$ (which is valid for $b \neq -1$). The constant of integration, c, doesn't matter for a definite integral because it would cancel out in the subtraction when evaluating the limits. The notation $\left[\frac{u^{16}}{16}\right]_{u=1}^{0}$ means to evaluate the antiderivative, $\frac{u^{16}}{16}$, at the limits ($u = 0$ and $u = 1$) and subtract:

$$-\left[\frac{u^{16}}{16}\right]_{u=1}^{0} + \left[\frac{u^{18}}{18}\right]_{u=1}^{0} = -\left(\frac{0^{16}}{16} - \frac{1^{16}}{16}\right) + \left(\frac{0^{18}}{18} - \frac{1^{18}}{18}\right) = -\left(0 - \frac{1}{16}\right) + \left(0 - \frac{1}{18}\right)$$

$$-\left(-\frac{1}{16}\right) + \left(-\frac{1}{18}\right) = \frac{1}{16} - \frac{1}{18} = \frac{1}{16}\frac{9}{9} - \frac{1}{18}\frac{8}{8} = \frac{9-8}{144} = \boxed{\frac{1}{144}} \approx \boxed{0.00694}$$

Date: ____________ Name: ______________________

Problem 9

Directions: For the curve below, find the slope of the tangent line at the point $\left(\frac{\pi}{3}, 1\right)$.

$$x - y \ln y + \sqrt{3} = \frac{\pi}{3} + \tan x$$

❖You can find the solution on the following page.

Solution to Problem 9

In order to determine the slope of the tangent line, we must calculate the derivative, $\frac{dy}{dx}$. For the given curve, you won't be able to isolate y by applying algebra. However, as we shalle see, it's still possible to isolate $\frac{dy}{dx}$. Take a derivative with respect to x on both sides of the equation.

$$\frac{d}{dx}\left(x - y\ln y + \sqrt{3}\right) = \frac{d}{dx}\left(\frac{\pi}{3} + \tan x\right) \quad \to \quad \frac{d}{dx}x - \frac{d}{dx}(y\ln y) + 0 = 0 + \frac{d}{dx}\tan x$$

Note that $\frac{d}{dx}x = 1$ and $\frac{d}{dx}\tan x = \sec^2 x$. Apply the product rule, $\frac{d}{dx}(fg) = f\frac{dg}{dx} + g\frac{df}{dx}$ with $f = y$ and $g = \ln y$.

$$1 - \left(y\frac{d}{dx}\ln y + \ln y\frac{dy}{dx}\right) = \sec^2 x$$

Apply the chain rule, $\frac{df}{dx} = \frac{df}{dy}\frac{dy}{dx}$, with $f = \ln y$, to write $\frac{d}{dx}\ln y = \frac{d}{dy}\ln y\frac{dy}{dx}$.

$$1 - \left(y\frac{d}{dy}\ln y\frac{dy}{dx} + \ln y\frac{dy}{dx}\right) = \sec^2 x$$

Note that $\frac{d}{dy}\ln y = \frac{1}{y}$.

$$1 - \left(\frac{y}{y}\frac{dy}{dx} + \ln y\frac{dy}{dx}\right) = \sec^2 x \quad \to \quad 1 - \left(\frac{dy}{dx} + \ln y\frac{dy}{dx}\right) = \sec^2 x$$

Add $\left(\frac{dy}{dx} + \ln y\frac{dy}{dx}\right)$ to both sides and subtract $\sec^2 x$ from both sides of the equation.

$$1 - \sec^2 x = \frac{dy}{dx} + \ln y\frac{dy}{dx}$$

Divide both sides of $\sin^2 x + \cos^2 x = 1$ by $\cos^2 x$ to get $\tan^2 x + 1 = \sec^2 x$. Subtract $\tan^2 x$ and $\sec^2 x$ from both sides to get $1 - \sec^2 x = -\tan^2 x$. Factor out $\frac{dy}{dx}$.

$$-\tan^2 x = \frac{dy}{dx} + \ln y\frac{dy}{dx} \quad \to \quad -\tan^2 x = (1 + \ln y)\frac{dy}{dx}$$

Divide both sides of the equation by $(1 + \ln y)$.

$$\frac{dy}{dx} = -\frac{\tan^2 x}{1 + \ln y}$$

Plug in $x = \frac{\pi}{3}$ and $y = 1$, corresponding to the point $\left(\frac{\pi}{3}, 1\right)$ specified in the problem.

$$\left.\frac{dy}{dx}\right|_{x=\frac{\pi}{3},\, y=1} = -\frac{\tan^2\left(\frac{\pi}{3}\right)}{1 + \ln 1} - \frac{\tan^2(60°)}{1 + \ln 1} = -\frac{\left(\sqrt{3}\right)^2}{1 + 0} = -\frac{3}{1} = \boxed{-3}$$

Date: ______________ Name: ______________________________

Problem 10

Directions: Perform the following derivative, assuming that $\sqrt{x} > 1$.

$$\frac{d}{dx}\sec^{-1}\sqrt{x}$$

Note: This is the inverse secant function (also called arcsecant). In this context, the $^{-1}$ doesn't mean to find a reciprocal. That is, $\sec^{-1}x$ doesn't mean the same as $\frac{1}{\sec x}$.

❖You can find the solution on the following page.

Solution to Problem 10

This is an application of the chain rule, involving inside and outside functions. After you take a derivative of the outside function, you then take a derivative of the inside function.

- The outside function, $f(u)$, is a secant inverse: $f(u) = \sec^{-1} u$.
- The inside function, $u(x)$, is a squareroot: $u(x) = \sqrt{x} = x^{1/2}$.

According to the chain rule, we multiply the two derivatives together:

$$\frac{df}{dx} = \frac{df}{du}\frac{du}{dx} = \left(\frac{d}{du}\sec^{-1} u\right)\left(\frac{d}{dx}x^{1/2}\right)$$

The derivative of the inverse secant function (or arcsecant function) is:

$$\frac{d}{du}\sec^{-1}(u) = \frac{1}{|u|\sqrt{u^2-1}} \text{ where } |u| > 1$$

Since the problem specified that $\sqrt{x} > 1$, and since $u = \sqrt{x}$, we know that u is positive in this problem. There is no reason to use absolute values: That is, $|u| = u$.

$$\frac{d}{du}\sec^{-1}(u) = \frac{1}{u\sqrt{u^2-1}} = \frac{1}{\sqrt{x}\sqrt{\left(\sqrt{x}\right)^2 - 1}} = \frac{1}{\sqrt{x}\sqrt{x-1}}$$

Substitute the above derivative into the equation for the chain rule.

$$\frac{df}{dx} = \frac{1}{\sqrt{x}\sqrt{x-1}}\left(\frac{d}{dx}x^{1/2}\right)$$

Apply the rule $\frac{d}{dx}ax^b = bax^{b-1}$. Note that $\frac{1}{x^n} = x^{-n}$, $x^{1/2} = \sqrt{x}$, and $\sqrt{x}\sqrt{x} = x$.

$$\frac{df}{dx} = \frac{1}{\sqrt{x}\sqrt{x-1}}\left(\frac{1}{2}x^{-1/2}\right) = \frac{1}{\sqrt{x}\sqrt{x-1}}\left(\frac{1}{2x^{1/2}}\right) = \frac{1}{\sqrt{x}\sqrt{x-1}}\left(\frac{1}{2\sqrt{x}}\right)$$

$$= \frac{1}{2\sqrt{x}\sqrt{x}\sqrt{x-1}} = \boxed{\frac{1}{2x\sqrt{x-1}}}$$

Multiply by $\frac{\sqrt{x-1}}{\sqrt{x-1}}$ in order to rationalize the denominator. Note that $\sqrt{x-1}\sqrt{x-1} = x - 1$ for the same reason that $\sqrt{y}\sqrt{y} = y$.

$$\frac{df}{dx} = \frac{1}{2x\sqrt{x-1}}\frac{\sqrt{x-1}}{\sqrt{x-1}} = \boxed{\frac{\sqrt{x-1}}{2x(x-1)}}$$

Date: ____________________ Name: ____

Problem 11

Directions: Perform the following integral.

$$\int \frac{dx}{9 - 4x^2}$$

❖You can find the solution on the following page.

Solution to Problem 11

An integral involving an expression of the form $a^2 - x^2$ can often be performed after making a substitution of the form $x = a\sin u$. The idea behind this substitution is to apply the identity $\sin^2 u + \cos^2 u = 1$ (as we will see in our solution). However, note that this integral has $9 - 4x^2$, which is different from $a^2 - x^2$. What we really have is $a^2 - b^2x^2$. Therefore, we need a substitution of the form $bx = a\sin\theta$. Plugging in $a = 3$ and $b = 2$ (since $a^2 = 9$ and $b^2 = 4$), we get $2x = 3\sin\theta$. Implicitly differentiate $2x = 3\sin\theta$ to get $2\,dx = 3\cos\theta\,d\theta$. (A derivative of $2x$ with respect to x equals 2, and a derivative of $3\sin\theta$ with respect to θ equals $3\cos\theta$.) Divide both sides of $2x = 3\sin\theta$ and $2\,dx = 3\cos\theta\,d\theta$ by 2 to get $x = \frac{3}{2}\sin\theta$ and $dx = \frac{3}{2}\cos\theta\,d\theta$. Substitute $x = \frac{3}{2}\sin\theta$ and $dx = \frac{3}{2}\cos\theta\,d\theta$ into the integral.

$$\int \frac{dx}{9 - 4x^2} = \int \frac{\frac{3}{2}\cos\theta\,d\theta}{9 - 4\left(\frac{3}{2}\sin\theta\right)^2}$$

Note that $\left(\frac{3}{2}\sin\theta\right)^2 = \frac{9}{4}\sin^2\theta$ because $(cx)^n = c^n x^n$.

$$\int \frac{\frac{3}{2}\cos\theta\,d\theta}{9 - 4\left(\frac{3}{2}\sin\theta\right)^2} = \frac{3}{2}\int \frac{\cos\theta\,d\theta}{9 - 4\left(\frac{9}{4}\right)\sin^2\theta} = \frac{3}{2}\int \frac{\cos\theta\,d\theta}{9 - 9\sin^2\theta}$$

Factor out the 9. Subtract $\sin^2\theta$ from both sides of the identity $\sin^2\theta + \cos^2\theta = 1$ to see that $\cos^2\theta = 1 - \sin^2\theta$. Note that $\frac{3}{18} = \frac{1}{6}$ and that $\frac{\cos\theta}{\cos^2\theta} = \frac{1}{\cos\theta} = \sec\theta$.

$$\frac{3}{2}\int \frac{\cos\theta\,d\theta}{9 - 9\sin^2\theta} = \frac{3}{2}\int \frac{\cos\theta\,d\theta}{9(1 - \sin^2\theta)} = \frac{3}{2(9)}\int \frac{\cos\theta\,d\theta}{1 - \sin^2\theta} = \frac{3}{18}\int \frac{\cos\theta\,d\theta}{\cos^2\theta}$$

$$\frac{3}{18}\int \frac{\cos\theta\,d\theta}{\cos^2\theta} = \frac{1}{6}\int \sec\theta\,d\theta = \frac{1}{6}\int \sec\theta\,d\theta = \frac{1}{6}\ln|\sec\theta + \tan\theta| + c$$

Since $2x = 3\sin\theta$, it follows that $\sin\theta = \frac{2x}{3}$. Since $\sin^2\theta + \cos^2\theta = 1$, it follows that $\cos\theta = \sqrt{1 - \sin^2\theta} = \sqrt{1 - \frac{4x^2}{9}} = \sqrt{\frac{9-4x^2}{9}} = \frac{\sqrt{9-4x^2}}{3}$ and $\tan\theta = \frac{\sin\theta}{\cos\theta} = \frac{2x/3}{\sqrt{9-4x^2}/3} = \frac{2x}{\sqrt{9-4x^2}}$. Note that $\sec\theta = \frac{1}{\cos\theta} = \frac{3}{\sqrt{9-4x^2}}$ such that $\sec\theta + \tan\theta = \frac{3+2x}{\sqrt{9-4x^2}}$.

$$\frac{1}{6}\ln|\sec\theta + \tan\theta| + c = \boxed{\frac{1}{6}\ln\left|\frac{3 + 2x}{\sqrt{9 - 4x^2}}\right| + c} = \boxed{\frac{1}{6}\ln\left|\sqrt{\frac{3 + 2x}{3 - 2x}}\right| + c} = \boxed{\frac{1}{12}\ln\left|\frac{3 + 2x}{3 - 2x}\right| + c}$$

Note that $(3 + 2x)(3 - 2x) = 9 - 4x^2$, such that $\frac{3+2x}{\sqrt{9-4x^2}} = \sqrt{\frac{3+2x}{3-2x}}$. Since $\ln\sqrt{y} = \ln y^{1/2} = \frac{1}{2}\ln y$ according to $\ln y^a = a\ln y$, it follows that $\frac{1}{6}\ln\left|\sqrt{\frac{3+2x}{3-2x}}\right| = \frac{1}{12}\ln\left|\frac{3+2x}{3-2x}\right|$.

Date: ____________________ Name: ____

Problem 12

Directions: Determine the area between the two curves shown in the graph below.

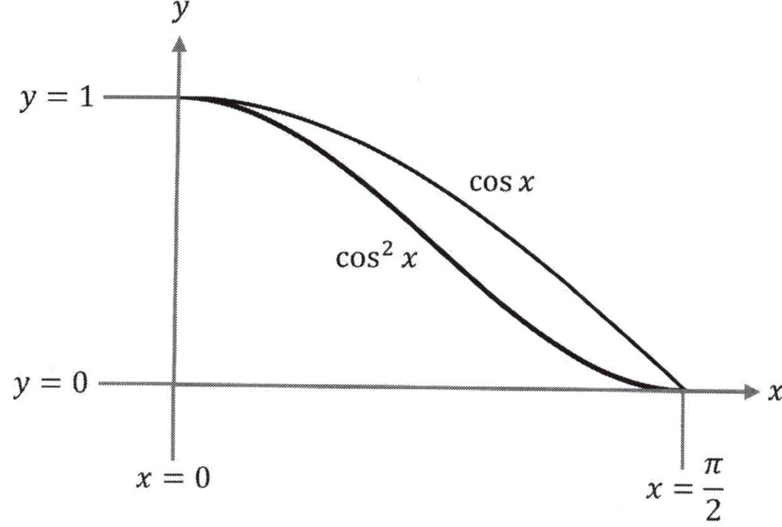

❖You can find the solution on the following page.

Solution to Problem 12

A definite integral equals the area between a curve and the horizontal axis. The area between two curves can thus be found by subtracting their definite integrals:

$$\Delta A = A_1 - A_2 = \int_{x=0}^{\pi/2} \cos x \, dx - \int_{x=0}^{\pi/2} \cos^2 x \, dx$$

The first integral is trivial:

$$A_1 = \int_{x=0}^{\pi/2} \cos x \, dx = [\sin x]_{x=0}^{\frac{\pi}{2}} = \sin\left(\frac{\pi}{2}\right) - \sin 0 = 1 - 0 = 1$$

The second integral is simpler if you apply the identity $\cos^2 x = \frac{1+\cos 2x}{2}$. (This handy trig identity helps with a variety of integrals. It's worth remembering.)

$$A_2 = \int_{x=0}^{\pi/2} \cos^2 x \, dx = \int_{x=0}^{\pi/2} \frac{1 + \cos 2x}{2} dx = \frac{1}{2} \int_{x=0}^{\pi/2} (1 + \cos 2x) \, dx$$

Separate this integral into two terms according to $\int (y_1 + y_2) \, dx = \int y_1 \, dx + \int y_2 \, dx$.

$$A_2 = \frac{1}{2} \int_{x=0}^{\pi/2} 1 \, dx + \frac{1}{2} \int_{x=0}^{\pi/2} \cos 2x \, dx = \frac{1}{2} [x]_{x=0}^{\frac{\pi}{2}} + \frac{1}{2} \int_{x=0}^{\pi/2} \cos 2x \, dx$$

For the second integral, make the substitution $\theta = 2x$, for which $d\theta = 2 \, dx$. Divide $d\theta = 2 \, dx$ by 2 to get $\frac{d\theta}{2} = dx$. Plug in $x = 0$ and $x = \frac{\pi}{2}$ to determine the new limits: $\theta_1 = 2(0) = 0$ and $\theta_2 = 2\left(\frac{\pi}{2}\right) = \pi$. Substitute $\theta = 2x$ and $\frac{d\theta}{2} = dx$ into the integral.

$$A_2 = \frac{1}{2}\left(\frac{\pi}{2} - 0\right) + \frac{1}{2} \int_{\theta=0}^{\pi} \cos \theta \frac{d\theta}{2} = \frac{1}{2}\left(\frac{\pi}{2}\right) + \frac{1}{4} \int_{\theta=0}^{\pi} \cos \theta \, d\theta = \frac{\pi}{4} + \frac{1}{4} [\sin \theta]_{\theta=0}^{\pi}$$

$$= \frac{\pi}{4} + \frac{1}{4}(\sin \pi - \sin 0) = \frac{\pi}{4} + \frac{1}{4}(0 - 0) = \frac{\pi}{4}$$

The area between the two curves equals the difference between the two areas:

$$\Delta A = A_1 - A_2 = 1 - \frac{\pi}{4} = \frac{4}{4} - \frac{\pi}{4} = \boxed{\frac{4 - \pi}{4}} \approx \boxed{0.215}$$

Date: ______________ Name: ______________________________

Problem 13

Directions: Perform the following derivative.

$$\frac{d}{dx}\ln[\ln(x^2 - 3x + 2)]$$

❖You can find the solution on the following page.

Solution to Problem 13

This is an application of the chain rule, involving inside and outside functions. It may help to review the solutions to Problems 1 and 10, for example. The current problem actually involves three functions:

- The outside function, $f(g)$, is a natural logarithm: $f(g) = \ln g$.
- The middle function, $g(u)$, is also a natural logarithm: $g(u) = \ln u$.
- The inside function, $u(x)$, is a polynomial: $u(x) = x^2 - 3x + 2$.

Watch how these three functions combine to form the given expression:

$$f = \ln g = \ln(\ln u) = \ln[\ln(x^2 - 3x + 2)]$$

According to the chain rule, we multiply the derivatives together:

$$\frac{df}{dx} = \frac{df}{dg}\frac{dg}{du}\frac{du}{dx} = \left(\frac{d}{dg}\ln g\right)\left(\frac{d}{du}\ln u\right)\left[\frac{d}{dx}(x^2 - 3x + 2)\right]$$

Recall from calculus that the derivative of the natural logarithm is: $\frac{d}{dx}\ln x = \frac{1}{x}$.

$$\frac{df}{dx} = \left(\frac{1}{g}\right)\left(\frac{1}{u}\right)(2x - 3) = \frac{2x - 3}{gu} = \frac{2x - 3}{(\ln u)(x^2 - 3x + 2)} = \frac{2x - 3}{(x^2 - 3x + 2)\ln u}$$

$$= \boxed{\frac{2x - 3}{(x^2 - 3x + 2)\ln(x^2 - 3x + 2)}}$$

Date: ____________________ Name: ____

Problem 14

Directions: Use the integral test to determine whether the following series converges or diverges.

$$\sum_{n=2}^{\infty} \frac{\ln n}{n\sqrt{n}}$$

❖You can find the solution on the following page.

Solution to Problem 14

Since $\frac{\ln n}{n\sqrt{n}}$ is a decreasing positive function (which you can verify by plugging in $n = 2$, $n = 3$, $n = 4$, etc.) and since the initial value ($n = 2$) is nonnegative, we may apply the integral test to determine whether or not the series converges. According to the integral test, the following improper integral will converge if the series converges and it will diverge if the series diverges.

$$\int_{x=2}^{\infty} \frac{\ln x}{x\sqrt{x}} dx$$

Note that $x\sqrt{x} = x^1 x^{1/2} = x^{1+1/2} = x^{3/2}$ because $x^m x^n = x^{m+n}$ and that $\frac{1}{x^{3/2}} = x^{-3/2}$ because $x^{-n} = \frac{1}{x^n}$.

$$\int_{x=2}^{\infty} \frac{\ln x}{x\sqrt{x}} dx = \int_{x=2}^{\infty} x^{-3/2} \ln x \, dx$$

Integrate by parts with $u = \ln x$ and $dv = x^{-3/2} dx$, for which $du = \frac{du}{dx} dx = \left(\frac{d}{dx} \ln x\right) dx = \frac{dx}{x}$ and $v = \int dv = \int x^{-3/2}\, dx = \frac{x^{-3/2+1}}{-\frac{3}{2}+1} = \frac{x^{-1/2}}{-1/2} = -2x^{-1/2}$ (since $1 \div \frac{1}{2} = 1 \times \frac{2}{1} = 2$).

$$\int_{x=2}^{\infty} u\, dv = [uv]_{x=2}^{\infty} - \int_{x=2}^{\infty} v\, du = \left[(\ln x)\left(-2x^{-1/2}\right)\right]_{x=2}^{\infty} - \int_{x=2}^{\infty} \left(-2x^{-1/2}\right) \frac{dx}{x}$$

$$= -2\left[x^{-1/2} \ln x\right]_{x=2}^{\infty} + 2 \int_{x=2}^{\infty} \frac{x^{-1/2}}{x} dx = -2\left[\frac{\ln x}{\sqrt{x}}\right]_{x=2}^{\infty} + 2 \int_{x=2}^{\infty} x^{-3/2}\, dx$$

$$= -2\left[\frac{\ln x}{\sqrt{x}}\right]_{x=2}^{\infty} + 2\left[-2x^{-\frac{1}{2}}\right]_{x=2}^{\infty} = -2\left[\frac{\ln x}{\sqrt{x}}\right]_{x=2}^{\infty} - 4\left[\frac{1}{\sqrt{x}}\right]_{x=2}^{\infty}$$

$$= -2\left[\lim_{x\to\infty}\left(\frac{\ln x}{\sqrt{x}}\right) - \frac{\ln 2}{\sqrt{2}}\right] - 4\left[\lim_{x\to\infty}\left(\frac{1}{\sqrt{x}}\right) - \frac{1}{\sqrt{2}}\right] = -2\left(0 - \frac{\ln 2}{\sqrt{2}}\right) - 4\left(0 - \frac{1}{\sqrt{2}}\right)$$

$$= -2\left(-\frac{\ln 2}{\sqrt{2}}\right) - 4\left(-\frac{1}{\sqrt{2}}\right) = \frac{2\ln 2}{\sqrt{2}} + \frac{4}{\sqrt{2}} = \sqrt{2}\ln 2 + 2\sqrt{2} = \boxed{\sqrt{2}(\ln 2 + 2)} \approx \boxed{3.809}$$

According to l'Hôpital's rule, $\lim_{x\to\infty}\left(\frac{\ln x}{\sqrt{x}}\right) = \frac{\frac{d}{dx}\ln x\big|_{x\to\infty}}{\frac{d}{dx}\sqrt{x}\big|_{x\to\infty}} = \frac{\frac{1}{x}}{\frac{1}{2\sqrt{x}}}\bigg|_{x\to\infty} = \frac{1}{x} \div \frac{1}{2\sqrt{x}}\bigg|_{x\to\infty} = \frac{2\sqrt{x}}{x}\bigg|_{x\to\infty} = \frac{2}{\sqrt{x}}\bigg|_{x\to\infty} = 0$. Since the integral is finite, the series $\boxed{\text{converges}}$.

Date: ______________ Name: ______________________________

Problem 15

Directions: Perform the following integral along the curve $y = 2x^3$.

$$\int_{x=0}^{1} y\sqrt{dx^2 + dy^2}$$

❖You can find the solution on the following page.

Solution to Problem 15

The trick to this integral is to factor out the dx. Note that this integral is similar to the arc length integral (except for the extra y in the integrand).

$$\int_{x=0}^{1} y\sqrt{dx^2+dy^2} = \int_{x=0}^{1} y\sqrt{\left[1+\left(\frac{dy}{dx}\right)^2\right]dx^2} = \int_{x=0}^{1} y\sqrt{\left[1+\left(\frac{dy}{dx}\right)^2\right]}\,dx$$

Find the derivative for the curve, $y = 2x^3$, specified in the problem. Apply the formula $\frac{d}{dx}ax^b = bax^{b-1}$ with $a = 2$ and $b = 3$.

$$\frac{dy}{dx} = \frac{d}{dx}(2x^3) = (3)(2)x^{3-1} = 6x^2$$

Substitute $y = 2x^3$ and $\frac{dy}{dx} = 6x^2$ into the previous integral.

$$\int_{x=0}^{1} 2x^3\sqrt{\left[1+\left(\frac{dy}{dx}\right)^2\right]}\,dx = 2\int_{x=0}^{1} x^3\sqrt{[1+(6x^2)^2]}\,dx$$

Note that $(6x^2)^2 = 6^2x^4 = 36x^4$ according to $(cx)^n = c^nx^n$ and $(x^m)^n = x^{mn}$.

$$2\int_{x=0}^{1} x^3\sqrt{[1+(6x^2)^2]}\,dx = 2\int_{x=0}^{1} x^3\sqrt{[1+36x^4]}\,dx$$

Make the substitution $u = 1 + 36x^4$. Implicitly differentiate $u = 1 + 36x^4$ to get $du = 144x^3\,dx$. (A derivative of $1 + 36x^4$ with respect to x equals $144x^3$.) Divide both sides of $du = 144x^3\,dx$ by $144x^3$ to get $\frac{du}{144x^3} = dx$. Use the equation $u = 1 + 36x^4$ to determine the new limits of integration:

$$u(0) = 1 + 36(0)^4 = 1 + 0 = 1 \quad , \quad u(1) = 1 + 36(1)^4 = 1 + 36 = 37$$

Substitute $u = 1 + 36x^4$ and $dx = \frac{du}{144x^3}$ into the integral.

$$2\int_{x=0}^{1} x^3\sqrt{[1+36x^4]}\,dx = 2\int_{u=1}^{37} x^3\sqrt{u}\frac{du}{144x^3} = \frac{2}{144}\int_{u=1}^{37} \frac{x^3\sqrt{u}}{x^3}du = \frac{1}{72}\int_{u=1}^{37} u^{1/2}\,du$$

$$= \frac{1}{72}\left[\frac{u^{1/2+1}}{\frac{1}{2}+1}\right]_{u=1}^{37} = \frac{1}{72}\left[\frac{u^{3/2}}{3/2}\right]_{u=1}^{37} = \frac{1}{72}\left[\frac{2u^{3/2}}{3}\right]_{u=1}^{37} = \frac{2}{216}\left[u^{3/2}\right]_{u=1}^{37} = \frac{1}{108}\left[u^{3/2}\right]_{u=1}^{37}$$

$$= \frac{1}{108}(37^{3/2} - 1^{3/2}) = \boxed{\frac{1}{108}(37^{3/2} - 1)} \approx \frac{225.062 - 1}{108} \approx \boxed{2.075}$$

Date: ________________ Name: ____________________________________

Problem 16

Directions: Perform the following sixty-third derivative.

$$\frac{d^{63}}{d\theta^{63}}\left(\frac{\sin 2\theta}{2^{60}}\right)$$

Note that 2 is raised to the power of 60 in the denominator. The sixty-third derivative is similar to a second derivative, except that it involves taking additional derivatives.

❖You can find the solution on the following page.

Solution to Problem 16

We need to take sixty-three consecutive derivatives of the given expression. Begin by taking the first derivative, which involves applying the chain rule with an outside function, $f(u) = \sin u$, and an inside function, $u(\theta) = 2\theta$.

$$\frac{d}{d\theta}\left(\frac{\sin 2\theta}{2^{60}}\right) = \frac{1}{2^{60}}\frac{d}{d\theta}(\sin 2\theta) = \frac{1}{2^{60}}\frac{df}{d\theta} = \frac{1}{2^{60}}\frac{df}{du}\frac{du}{d\theta}$$

$$= \frac{1}{2^{60}}\left(\frac{d}{du}\sin u\right)\left(\frac{d}{d\theta}2\theta\right) = \frac{1}{2^{60}}(\cos u)(2) = \frac{2\cos 2\theta}{2^{60}}$$

Let's work out the first few derivatives in order to help see what pattern emerges.

$$\frac{d}{d\theta}\left(\frac{\sin 2\theta}{2^{60}}\right) = \frac{2\cos 2\theta}{2^{60}} = \frac{\cos 2\theta}{2^{59}}$$

$$\frac{d^2}{d\theta^2}\left(\frac{\sin 2\theta}{2^{60}}\right) = \frac{d}{d\theta}\left(\frac{\cos 2\theta}{2^{59}}\right) = -\frac{2^2 \sin 2\theta}{2^{60}} = -\frac{\sin 2\theta}{2^{58}}$$

$$\frac{d^3}{d\theta^3}\left(\frac{\sin 2\theta}{2^{60}}\right) = \frac{d}{d\theta}\left(-\frac{\sin 2\theta}{2^{58}}\right) = -\frac{2^3 \cos 2\theta}{2^{60}} = -\frac{\cos 2\theta}{2^{57}}$$

$$\frac{d^4}{d\theta^4}\left(\frac{\sin 2\theta}{2^{60}}\right) = \frac{d}{d\theta}\left(-\frac{\cos 2\theta}{2^{57}}\right) = \frac{2^4 \sin 2\theta}{2^{60}} = \frac{\sin 2\theta}{2^{56}}$$

You should make two observations:

- From the chain rule, each time that we take a derivative of a trig function, a factor of 2 appears from the derivative of the inside function, since $\frac{d}{d\theta}2\theta = 2$ (just as $\frac{d}{dx}2x = 2$). The nth derivative will bring out 2^n.
- Every even-numbered derivative adds another minus sign because $\frac{d}{d\theta}\sin\theta = \cos\theta$ while $\frac{d}{d\theta}\cos\theta = -\sin\theta$. Every 4 derivatives go through the following pattern: positive cosine, negative sine, negative cosine, positive sine.

What will happen with the sixty-third derivative?

- 2^{63} will come out from applying the chain rule 63 times.
- The 63rd derivative will have the same trig function as the 3rd derivative since 63 divided by 4 has a remainder of 3. The 3rd derivative, 7th derivative, 11th derivative, and so on, including the 63rd derivative, will all have $-\cos 2\theta$ since every 4th derivative repeats the same combination of trig function and sign.

$$\frac{d^{63}}{dx^{63}}\left(\frac{\sin 2\theta}{2^{60}}\right) = -\frac{2^{63}\cos 2\theta}{2^{60}} = -2^{63-60}\cos 2\theta = -2^3\cos 2\theta = \boxed{-8\cos 2\theta}$$

Date: ________________ Name: ______________________________________

Problem 17

Directions: Perform the following double integral.

$$\int_{x=1}^{2}\int_{y=x}^{4x}\frac{dxdy}{(8x-3y)^3}$$

❖You can find the solution on the following page.

Solution to Problem 17

We must perform the integral over y first because the upper limit of the y integral contains the variable x. When we integrate over y, we treat the independent variable x as if it were a constant. We may also change the order of $dxdy$: It's the limits (not the differentials) that determines the order of integration.

$$\int_{x=1}^{2}\int_{y=x}^{4x}\frac{dxdy}{(8x-3y)^3}=\int_{x=1}^{2}\left(\int_{y=x}^{4x}\frac{dy}{(8x-3y)^3}\right)dx$$

Make the substitution $u = 8x - 3y$. Implicitly differentiate $u = 8x - 3y$ (temporarily treating x as a constant, which we are permitted to do when integrating over y) to get $du = -3\,dy$. (A derivative of $8x - 3y$ with respect to y equals -3 when treating x as a constant.) Divide both sides of the equation $du = -3\,dy$ by -3 to get $-\frac{du}{3} = dy$.

Use the equation $u = 8x - 3y$ to determine the new limits for the y integral:

$$u(x) = 8x - 3(x) = 8x - 3x = 5x \quad , \quad u(4x) = 8x - 3(4x) = 8x - 12x = -4x$$

Substitute $u = 8x - 3y$ and $-\frac{du}{3} = dy$ into the integral.

$$\int_{x=1}^{2}\left(\int_{y=x}^{4x}\frac{dy}{(8x-3y)^3}\right)dx=\int_{x=1}^{2}\left(\int_{u=5x}^{-4x}\frac{-du/3}{u^3}\right)dx=-\frac{1}{3}\int_{x=1}^{2}\left(\int_{u=5x}^{-4x}\frac{du}{u^3}\right)dx$$

$$=-\frac{1}{3}\int_{x=1}^{2}\left(\int_{u=5x}^{-4x}u^{-3}\,du\right)dx=-\frac{1}{3}\int_{x=1}^{2}\left[\frac{u^{-3+1}}{-3+1}\right]_{u=5x}^{-4x}dx=-\frac{1}{3}\int_{x=1}^{2}\left[\frac{u^{-2}}{-2}\right]_{u=5x}^{-4x}dx$$

$$=\frac{1}{3(2)}\int_{x=1}^{2}[u^{-2}]_{u=5x}^{-4x}\,dx=\frac{1}{6}\int_{x=1}^{2}\left[\frac{1}{u^2}\right]_{u=5x}^{-4x}dx=\frac{1}{6}\int_{x=1}^{2}\left[\frac{1}{(-4x)^2}-\frac{1}{(5x)^2}\right]dx$$

$$=\frac{1}{6}\int_{x=1}^{2}\left(\frac{1}{16x^2}-\frac{1}{25x^2}\right)dx=\frac{1}{6}\int_{x=1}^{2}\left(\frac{25-16}{400x^2}\right)dx=\frac{1}{6}\int_{x=1}^{2}\frac{9}{400x^2}dx=\frac{9}{2400}\int_{x=1}^{2}\frac{dx}{x^2}$$

$$=\frac{3}{800}\int_{x=1}^{2}x^{-2}\,dx=\frac{3}{800}\left[\frac{x^{-2+1}}{-2+1}\right]_{x=1}^{2}=\frac{3}{800}\left[\frac{x^{-1}}{-1}\right]_{x=1}^{2}=-\frac{3}{800}[x^{-1}]_{x=1}^{2}$$

$$=-\frac{3}{800}\left[\frac{1}{x}\right]_{x=1}^{2}=-\frac{3}{800}\left(\frac{1}{2}-\frac{1}{1}\right)=-\frac{3}{800}\left(\frac{1-2}{2}\right)=-\frac{3}{800}\left(-\frac{1}{2}\right)$$

$$=\boxed{\frac{3}{1600}}\approx\boxed{0.001875}$$

Date: ____________ Name: ______________________

Problem 18

Directions: A monkey throws a rope over a horizontal bar, and ties one end of the rope to a bunch of bananas, as illustrated below. When the monkey walks to the right with a constant speed of 6 m/s, the bananas travel upward. The horizontal bar is positioned 12 m higher than the monkey's head. Show that the speed of the bananas is given by the formula below, where x represents the horizontal distance from the monkey to the bananas.

$$\frac{dy}{dt} = \frac{6x}{\sqrt{x^2 + 144}}$$

(bar is perpendicular to the page)

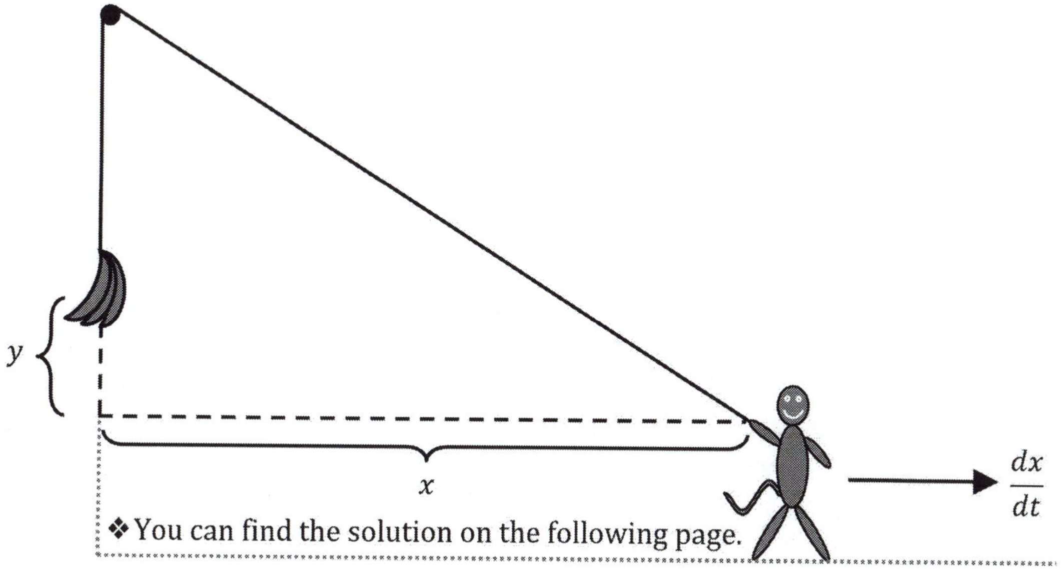

y

x

$\frac{dx}{dt}$

❖ You can find the solution on the following page.

Solution to Problem 18

The horizontal distance, x, is related to the height of the horizontal bar, 12 m, through the right triangle shown below.

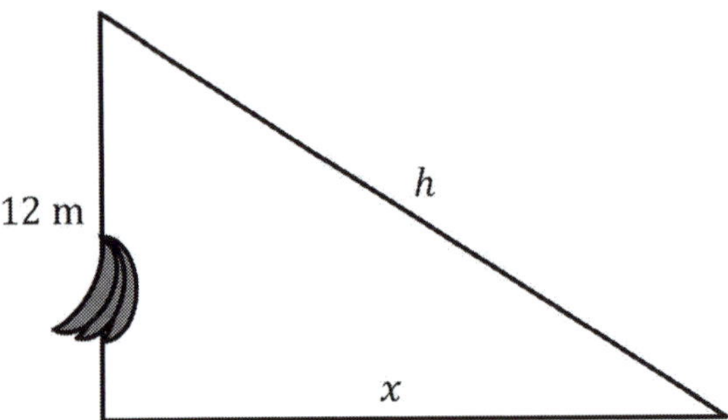

According to the Pythagorean theorem, the hypotenuse of the triangle is:

$$h = \sqrt{x^2 + 12^2} = \sqrt{x^2 + 144}$$

Note that the speed of the bananas, $\frac{dy}{dt}$, equals the rate at which the hypotenuse gets longer, $\frac{dh}{dt}$. Why? Because the monkey is pulling the rope: The bananas rise exactly the same distance that the hypotenuse grows (so that the total length of the rope remains constant).

$$\frac{dy}{dt} = \frac{dh}{dt}$$

Find the derivative $\frac{dh}{dt}$ using the chain rule:

$$\frac{dy}{dt} = \frac{dh}{dt} = \frac{dh}{dx}\frac{dx}{dt} = \left(\frac{d}{dx}\sqrt{x^2 + 144}\right)\left(\frac{dx}{dt}\right)$$

According to the problem, the speed of the monkey is $\frac{dx}{dt} = 6$ (in units of m/s).

$$\frac{dy}{dt} = \left(\frac{d}{dx}\sqrt{x^2 + 144}\right)(6) = 6\frac{d}{dx}\sqrt{x^2 + 144}$$

Apply the chain rule with $f = \sqrt{u} = u^{1/2}$ and $u = x^2 + 144$:

$$\frac{dy}{dt} = 6\frac{df}{dx} = 6\frac{df}{du}\frac{du}{dx} = 6\left(\frac{d}{du}u^{1/2}\right)\left[\frac{d}{dx}(x^2 + 144)\right] = 6\left(\frac{1}{2}\right)u^{-1/2}(2x) = 6xu^{-1/2}$$

$$\frac{dy}{dt} = \frac{6x}{u^{1/2}} = \frac{6x}{\sqrt{u}} = \boxed{\frac{6x}{\sqrt{x^2 + 144}}}$$

In calculus, problems like this are called "related rates."

Date: ________________ Name: ____________________________________

Problem 19

Directions: Perform the following integral.

$$\int e^{-x} \cos x \, dx$$

❖You can find the solution on the following page.

Solution to Problem 19

Integrate by parts with $u = e^{-x}$ and $dv = \cos x\, dx$, for which:

$$du = \frac{du}{dx}dx = \left(\frac{d}{dx}e^{-x}\right)dx = -e^{-x}dx$$

$$v = \int dv = \int \cos x\, dx = \sin x$$

The formula for integration by parts is:

$$\int u\, dv = uv - \int v\, du$$

Substitute $u = e^{-x}$, $v = \sin x$, $du = -e^{-x}dx$, and $dv = \cos x\, dx$ into the equation for integration by parts:

$$\int e^{-x} \cos x\, dx = e^{-x} \sin x - \int \sin x\,(-e^{-x}dx)$$

$$\int e^{-x} \cos x\, dx = e^{-x} \sin x + \int e^{-x} \sin x\, dx$$

Integrate by parts a second time with $u = e^{-x}$ and $dw = \sin x\, dx$, for which:

$$du = \frac{du}{dx}dx = \left(\frac{d}{dx}e^{-x}\right)dx = -e^{-x}dx$$

$$w = \int dw = \int \sin x\, dx = -\cos x$$

$$\int e^{-x} \sin x\, dx = uw - \int w\, du = e^{-x}(-\cos x) - \int (-\cos x)\,(-e^{-x}dx)$$

$$\int e^{-x} \sin x\, dx = -e^{-x} \cos x - \int e^{-x} \cos x\, dx$$

Substitute the above equation into the original equation from integration by parts:

$$\int e^{-x} \cos x\, dx = e^{-x} \sin x + \int e^{-x} \sin x\, dx$$

$$\int e^{-x} \cos x\, dx = e^{-x} \sin x - e^{-x} \cos x - \int e^{-x} \cos x\, dx$$

Add $\int e^{-x} \cos x\, dx$ to both sides of the equation, then divide both sides by 2.

$$2\int e^{-x} \cos x\, dx = e^{-x} \sin x - e^{-x} \cos x$$

$$\int e^{-x} \cos x\, dx = \frac{e^{-x} \sin x - e^{-x} \cos x}{2} + c = \boxed{\frac{e^{-x}(\sin x - \cos x)}{2} + c}$$

As usual with an indefinite integral, there is an arbitrary constant of integration.

Date: ____________ Name: ______________________________

Problem 20

Directions: Evaluate the following limit.

$$\lim_{x \to 0^+} x^x$$

Note: This is a one-sided limit. The notation $x \to c^+$ means "as x approaches c from the right" (corresponding to values of $x > c$).

❖You can find the solution on the following page.

Solution to Problem 20

A limit of the form $\lim_{x \to c} f(x)$ doesn't mean to simply plug $x = c$ into the function $f(x)$ to determine $f(c)$. Although that may work in specific cases, that doesn't work in all cases. This is one of those cases. A limit of the form $\lim_{x \to c} f(x)$ really asks, "What value does $f(x)$ approach as x gets closer and closer to c?"

Are you thinking something like, "Anything to the power of zero equals one"? If so, this isn't quite true. Although $8^0 = 1$, $1^0 = 1$, and $0.5^0 = 1$, not every number raised to the power of zero equals one. There is one exception: zero to the power of zero (0^0) is indeterminate. When you see x^0, it only equals 1 if $x \neq 0$. Why? Consider the ratio $\frac{x^n}{x^n}$. According to the rule $\frac{x^n}{x^m} = x^{n-m}$, we can write $\frac{x^n}{x^n} = x^{n-n} = x^0$. The reason that $x^0 = 1$ for nonzero values of x is that $\frac{x^n}{x^n} = 1$ for nonzero values of x. But when $x = 0$, the ratio $\frac{x^n}{x^n}$ (which is the same as x^0) is indeterminate, for the same reason that $0/0$ is indeterminate. (You know that $12/4$, which equals 3, means the same as, "What times 4 equals 12?" Similarly, $0/0$ means the same as, "What times 0 equals 0?" The reason that $0/0$ is indeterminate is that anything times 0 equals 0. Since 3, 9, 500, and any other number times 0 equals 0, you can't determine which answer is the 'correct' answer to $0/0$.)

The trick to this problem is to recall the rule $e^{\ln y} = y$. Let $y = x^x$ to get $e^{\ln x^x} = x^x$. Also recall the rule $\ln x^p = p \ln x$. Let $p = x$ to get $\ln x^x = x \ln x$. Now substitute $\ln x^x = x \ln x$ into $e^{\ln x^x} = x^x$ to get $e^{x \ln x} = x^x$. Thus, $\lim_{x \to 0^+} x^x = \lim_{x \to 0^+} e^{x \ln x} = e^{\lim_{x \to 0^+} x \ln x}$. Since $\lim_{x \to 0^+} x \ln x$ is indeterminate, we may apply l'Hôpital's rule.

$$\lim_{x \to 0^+} x \ln x = \lim_{x \to 0^+} \frac{\ln x}{1/x} = \lim_{x \to 0^+} \frac{\frac{d}{dx} \ln x}{\frac{d}{dx} \frac{1}{x}} = \lim_{x \to 0^+} \frac{\frac{1}{x}}{-\frac{1}{x^2}}$$

To divide by a fraction, multiply by its reciprocal: $\frac{\frac{1}{x}}{-\frac{1}{x^2}} = \frac{1}{x}\left(-\frac{x^2}{1}\right) = \frac{1}{x}(-x^2) = -\frac{x^2}{x}$.

$$\lim_{x \to 0^+} x \ln x = \lim_{x \to 0^+} \frac{1}{x}(-x^2) = \lim_{x \to 0^+} (-x) = 0 \quad \text{(note: this is **not** the final answer)}$$

Finally, plug $\lim_{x \to 0^+} x \ln x = 0$ into $\lim_{x \to 0^+} x^x = e^{\lim_{x \to 0^+} x \ln x}$ to get $\lim_{x \to 0^+} x^x = e^0 = \boxed{1}$. You can numerically verify that $\lim_{x \to 0^+} x^x = \boxed{1}$ by entering smaller and smaller values of x on your calculator. Think about it: What's the problem with evaluating this limit from the left? (Try letting $x = -\frac{1}{2}$ and you may discover the challenge.)

Date: ______________ Name: ______________________________

Problem 21

Directions: Perform the following derivative.

$$\frac{d}{d\psi}\sqrt{\frac{\sinh^2\psi}{\cosh^2\psi} + 5e^{-\pi^2} - 8\ln\pi^3 + \operatorname{sech}^2\psi}$$

Note: $\sinh x$, $\cosh x$, and $\operatorname{sech} x$ are hyperbolic functions (not to be confused with the ordinary trig functions $\sin x$, $\cos x$, and $\sec x$). The h in $\sinh x$ makes a big difference.

❖You can find the solution on the following page.

Solution to Problem 21

Recall how the hyperbolic functions are defined:

$$\cosh x = \frac{e^x + e^{-x}}{2} \quad , \quad \sinh x = \frac{e^x - e^{-x}}{2} \quad , \quad \operatorname{sech} x = \frac{1}{\cosh x}$$

The following identity will be helpful for the given problem:

$$\cosh^2 x - \sinh^2 x = \left(\frac{e^x + e^{-x}}{2}\right)^2 - \left(\frac{e^x - e^{-x}}{2}\right)^2$$

$$\cosh^2 x - \sinh^2 x = \frac{e^{2x} + 2e^x e^{-x} + e^{-2x}}{4} - \frac{e^{2x} - 2e^x e^{-x} + e^{-2x}}{4}$$

$$\cosh^2 x - \sinh^2 x = \frac{e^{2x} + 2 + e^{-2x}}{4} - \frac{e^{2x} - 2 + e^{-2x}}{4}$$

$$\cosh^2 x - \sinh^2 x = \frac{e^{2x} + 2 + e^{-2x} - (e^{2x} - 2 + e^{-2x})}{4}$$

$$\cosh^2 x - \sinh^2 x = \frac{e^{2x} + 2 + e^{-2x} - e^{2x} - (-2) - e^{-2x}}{4}$$

$$\cosh^2 x - \sinh^2 x = \frac{e^{2x} + 2 + e^{-2x} - e^{2x} + 2 - e^{-2x}}{4} = \frac{2+2}{4} = \frac{4}{4} = 1$$

Compare the hyperbolic identity, $\cosh^2 x - \sinh^2 x = 1$, to the ordinary trig identity, $\cos^2 x + \sin^2 x = 1$. Note that the hyperbolic identity has a minus sign. Examine the expression given in the problem, which includes:

$$\frac{\sinh^2 \psi}{\cosh^2 \psi} + \operatorname{sech}^2 \psi = \frac{\sinh^2 \psi}{\cosh^2 \psi} + \frac{1}{\cosh^2 \psi} = \frac{\sinh^2 \psi + 1}{\cosh^2 \psi}$$

Add $\sinh^2 x$ to both sides of $\cosh^2 x - \sinh^2 x = 1$ to see that $\cosh^2 x = \sinh^2 x + 1$. In the previous equation, the numerator is the same as $\cosh^2 \psi$.

$$\frac{\sinh^2 \psi}{\cosh^2 \psi} + \operatorname{sech}^2 \psi = \frac{\sinh^2 \psi + 1}{\cosh^2 \psi} = \frac{\cosh^2 \psi}{\cosh^2 \psi} = 1$$

Since $\frac{\sinh^2 \psi}{\cosh^2 \psi} + \operatorname{sech}^2 \psi = 1$ and since π is a constant, it turns out that the expression given in the problem is constant (the only variable, ψ, canceled out). The derivative of any constant equals zero.

$$\frac{d}{d\psi}\sqrt{\frac{\sinh^2 \psi}{\cosh^2 \psi} + 5e^{-\pi^2} - 8\ln \pi^3 + \operatorname{sech}^2 \psi} = \frac{d}{d\psi}\sqrt{1 + 5e^{-\pi^2} - 8\ln \pi^3} = \boxed{0}$$

Date: ________________ Name: ______________________________________

Problem 22

Directions: Perform the following integral as instructed in each part below.

$$\int_i^f 12xy^2\,(3dx - 2dy)$$

(A) Integrate from (1,3) to (2,5) along the straight line $y = 2x + 1$.

(B) Integrate along the path $(1,3) \rightarrow (2,3) \rightarrow (2,5)$, which consists of a horizontal line followed by a vertical line.

❖You can find the solution on the following page.

Solution to Problem 22

Separate the given integral into two integrals:

$$\int_i^f 12xy^2\,(3dx - 2dy) = \int_i^f 12xy^2\,3dx - \int_i^f 12xy^2\,2dy = 36\int_i^f xy^2\,dx - 24\int_i^f xy^2\,dy$$

Note: Don't pull x out of the y integral or vice-versa. Why not? Because (unlike a double integral of the form $\iint x^3y^2\,dxdy$), the variables x and y are not independent here. You can see the dependence in the equation $y = 2x + 1$ given in part (A), for example.

Note: It is incorrect to visually find the area under the specified paths. For example, the area under $y = 2x + 1$ in (A) would be $\int_{x=1}^{2}(2x+1)\,dx$, not $\int_i^f 12xy^2\,(3dx - 2dy)$.

(A) For the integral over dx, plug in $y = 2x + 1$ and integrate from $x = 1$ to $x = 2$ (these values come from the given coordinates). For the integral over dy, plug in $x = \frac{y-1}{2}$ and integrate from $y = 3$ to $y = 5$. (Note that $x = \frac{y-1}{2}$ comes from solving for x in $y = 2x + 1$.)

$$36\int_i^f xy^2\,dx - 24\int_i^f xy^2\,dy = 36\int_{x=1}^{2} x(2x+1)^2\,dx - 24\int_{y=3}^{5}\left(\frac{y-1}{2}\right)y^2\,dy$$

$$= 36\int_{x=1}^{2} x(4x^2+4x+1)\,dx - 12\int_{y=3}^{5}(y-1)y^2\,dy = 36\int_{x=1}^{2}(4x^3+4x^2+x)\,dx - 12\int_{y=3}^{5}(y^3-y^2)\,dy$$

$$= 36\left[x^4 + \frac{4x^3}{3} + \frac{x^2}{2}\right]_{x=1}^{2} - 12\left[\frac{y^4}{4} - \frac{y^3}{3}\right]_{y=3}^{5} = [36x^4 + 48x^3 + 18x^2]_{x=1}^{2} - [3y^4 - 4y^3]_{y=3}^{5}$$

$$= [36(2^4) + 48(2^3) + 18(2^2) - 36(1^4) - 48(1^3) - 18(1^2)] - [3(5^4) - 4(5^3) - 3(3^4) + 4(3^3)]$$

$$= (576 + 384 + 72 - 36 - 48 - 18) - (1875 - 500 - 243 + 108) = 930 - 1240 = \boxed{-310}$$

(B) Along the horizontal line $(1,3) \to (2,3)$, only the first integral matters (since y is constant): Plug in $y = 3$. Along the vertical line $(2,3) \to (2,5)$, only the second integral matters (since x is constant): Plug in $x = 2$.

$$36\int_i^f xy^2\,dx - 24\int_i^f xy^2\,dy = 36\int_{x=1}^{2} x(3)^2\,dx - 24\int_{y=3}^{5}(2)y^2\,dy$$

$$= 324\int_{x=1}^{2} x\,dx - 48\int_{y=3}^{5} y^2\,dy = 324\left[\frac{x^2}{2}\right]_{x=1}^{2} - 48\left[\frac{y^3}{3}\right]_{y=3}^{5} = 162[x^2]_{x=1}^{2} - 16[y^3]_{y=3}^{5}$$

$$= 162(2^2 - 1^2) - 16(5^3 - 3^3) = 162(4-1) - 16(125-27) = 486 - 1568 = \boxed{-1082}$$

Date: ________________ Name: ______________________________________

Problem 23

Directions: Perform the following derivative (assuming $x \neq 1$).

$$\frac{d}{dx}\sqrt{\frac{\sqrt{x}+\frac{1}{\sqrt{x}}}{\sqrt{x}-\frac{1}{\sqrt{x}}}}$$

❖You can find the solution on the following page.

Solution to Problem 23

Before we take the derivative, let's multiply both the numerator and denominator of the fraction by $\sqrt{x}$. (We're effectively multiplying the fraction by one since $\frac{\sqrt{x}}{\sqrt{x}} = 1$.)

$$\frac{d}{dx}\sqrt{\frac{\sqrt{x}+\frac{1}{\sqrt{x}}}{\sqrt{x}-\frac{1}{\sqrt{x}}}} = \frac{d}{dx}\sqrt{\frac{\left(\sqrt{x}+\frac{1}{\sqrt{x}}\right)\sqrt{x}}{\left(\sqrt{x}-\frac{1}{\sqrt{x}}\right)\sqrt{x}}} = \frac{d}{dx}\sqrt{\frac{\sqrt{x}\sqrt{x}+\frac{\sqrt{x}}{\sqrt{x}}}{\sqrt{x}\sqrt{x}-\frac{\sqrt{x}}{\sqrt{x}}}} = \frac{d}{dx}\sqrt{\frac{x+1}{x-1}}$$

Apply the chain rule, with $f(u) = \sqrt{u} = u^{1/2}$ and $u(x) = \frac{x+1}{x-1}$.

$$\frac{d}{dx}\sqrt{\frac{x+1}{x-1}} = \frac{df}{dx} = \frac{df}{du}\frac{du}{dx} = \left(\frac{d}{du}u^{1/2}\right)\left[\frac{d}{dx}\left(\frac{x+1}{x-1}\right)\right] = \left(\frac{1}{2}u^{-1/2}\right)\left[\frac{d}{dx}\left(\frac{x+1}{x-1}\right)\right]$$

$$= \left(\frac{1}{2\sqrt{u}}\right)\left[\frac{d}{dx}\left(\frac{x+1}{x-1}\right)\right] = \left(\frac{1}{2\sqrt{\frac{x+1}{x-1}}}\right)\left[\frac{d}{dx}\left(\frac{x+1}{x-1}\right)\right] = \frac{1}{2}\sqrt{\frac{x-1}{x+1}}\left[\frac{d}{dx}\left(\frac{x+1}{x-1}\right)\right]$$

Apply the quotient rule with $p(x) = x + 1$ and $q(x) = x - 1$.

$$\frac{d}{dx}\left(\frac{p}{q}\right) = \frac{q\frac{dp}{dx} - p\frac{dq}{dx}}{q^2} = \frac{(x-1)\frac{d}{dx}(x+1) - (x+1)\frac{d}{dx}(x-1)}{(x-1)^2}$$

$$= \frac{(x-1)(1) - (x+1)(1)}{(x-1)^2} = \frac{x-1-x-1}{(x-1)^2} = \frac{-2}{(x-1)^2}$$

Substitute $\frac{d}{dx}\frac{x+1}{x-1} = \frac{-2}{(x^2-1)^2}$ into the expression for $\frac{df}{dx}$ (from the chain rule).

$$\frac{df}{dx} = \frac{1}{2}\sqrt{\frac{x-1}{x+1}}\frac{(-2)}{(x-1)^2} = \sqrt{\frac{x-1}{x+1}}\frac{(-1)}{(x-1)^2}$$

Multiply the fraction in the squareroot by $\frac{(x+1)}{(x+1)}$ in order to rationalize the denominator.

Note that $\sqrt{(x+1)^2} = x + 1$.

$$\frac{df}{dx} = \sqrt{\frac{(x-1)(x+1)}{(x+1)(x+1)}}\frac{(-1)}{(x-1)^2} = \frac{\sqrt{x^2+x-x-1}}{\sqrt{(x+1)^2}}\frac{(-1)}{(x-1)^2}$$

$$= \frac{\sqrt{x^2-1}}{(x+1)}\frac{(-1)}{(x-1)^2} = \boxed{\frac{-\sqrt{x^2-1}}{(x+1)(x-1)^2}}$$

The answer could alternatively be expressed as $\frac{-1}{\sqrt{x+1}(x-1)^{3/2}}$.

Date: ____________________ Name: ____

Problem 24

Directions: Solve for y as a function of x, given that $y(4) = -1$.

$$dy + 6\,dx = -3y\,dx$$

❖You can find the solution on the following page.

Solution to Problem 24

This first-order differential equation can be solved by the technique of separation of variables. This means to apply algebra to put the variables x and y on opposite sides of the equation. First subtract 6 dx from both sides of the equation.

$$dy + 6\,dx = -3y\,dx \quad \to \quad dy = -3y\,dx - 6\,dx$$

Factor out $-3\,dx$. Note that $(y+2)(-3) = -3y - 6$.

$$dy = (y+2)(-3\,dx)$$

Divide both sides of the equation by $y + 2$.

$$\frac{dy}{y+2} = -3\,dx$$

Now that we have separated variables, we may integrate both sides of the equation.

$$\int \frac{dy}{y+2} = -\int 3\,dx$$

For the first integral, we will make the substitution $u = y + 2$, for which $du = dy$.

$$\int \frac{du}{u} = -3\int dx$$

The integral $\int \frac{du}{u} = \ln u$ because $\frac{d}{du}\ln u = \frac{1}{u}$, while the integral $\int dx = x$. There is also a constant of integration, which we shall call c.

$$\ln u = -3x + c$$

Exponentiate both sides of the equation.

$$e^{\ln u} = e^{-3x+c}$$

Recall the identity $e^{\ln u} = u$.

$$u = e^{-3x+c}$$

Make the substitution $u = y + 2$.

$$y + 2 = e^{-3x+c}$$

Subtract 2 from both sides of the equation.

$$y = e^{-3x+c} - 2$$

Apply the given boundary condition, $y(4) = -1$, in order to determine the constant c. The condition $y(4) = -1$ means to set $x = 4$ and $y = -1$.

$$-1 = e^{-3(4)+c} - 2 \quad \to \quad 1 = e^{-12+c} \quad \to \quad -12 + c = 0 \quad \to \quad c = 12$$

We applied the identity $e^0 = 1$ to determine that $-12 + c = 0$. Our final answer is:

$$\boxed{y(x) = e^{-3x+12} - 2}$$

Date: ____________________ Name: ____________________

Problem 25

Directions: Determine the area between the parabola and the line $y = 4$ shown in the graph below.

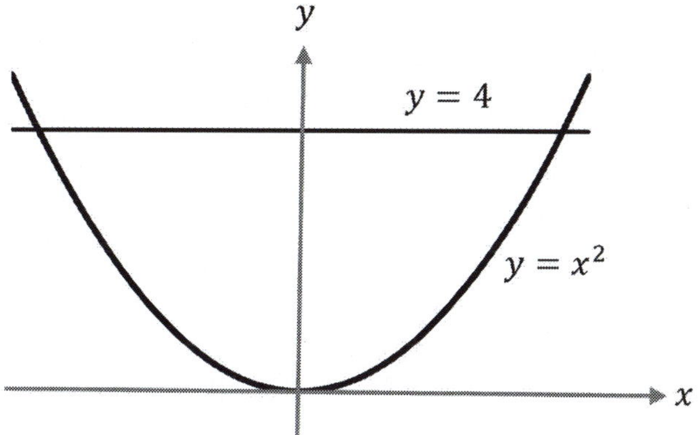

❖You can find the solution on the following page.

Solution to Problem 25

The area between the parabola, $y = x^2$, and horizontal line, $y = 4$, can be expressed as a double integral. (It's also possible to find the area with a single integral. We will explore that later in our solution.) Imagine dividing the region between the parabola and line into a very large number of tiny rectangles with area $dA = dxdy$. We wish to add up the areas of all the tiny rectangles in $-2 \leq x < 2$ (since $x = \pm 2$ corresponds to $y = x^2 = 4$). For a given value of x, the variable y ranges from $y = x^2$ to $y = 4$.

$$A = \int dA = \int_{x=-2}^{2} \int_{y=x^2}^{4} dy\, dx$$

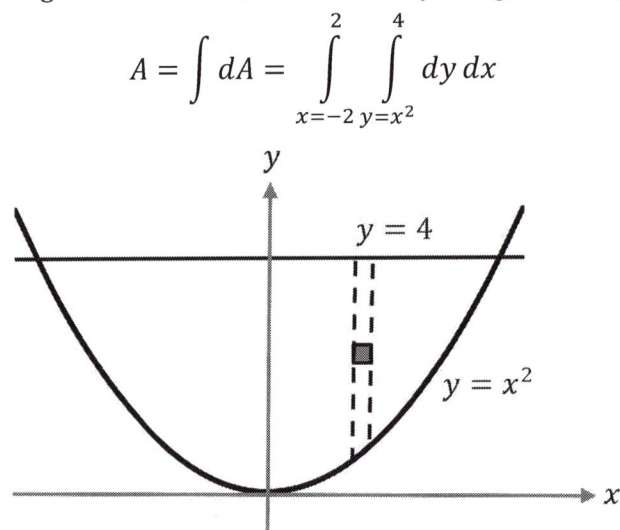

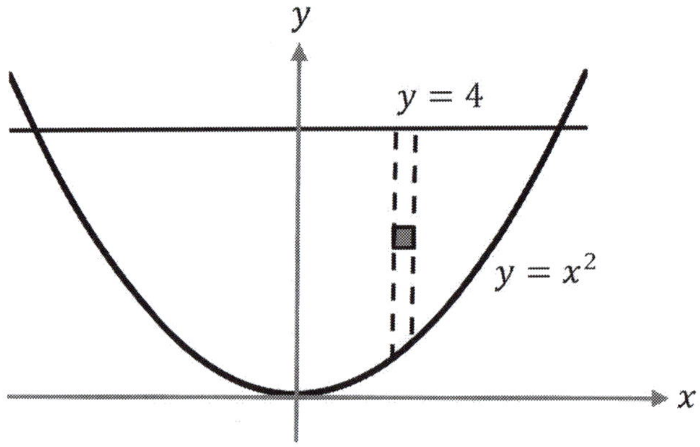

We must integrate over the variable y first because its lower limit is x^2.

$$A = \int_{x=-2}^{2} [y]_{y=x^2}^{4}\, dx = \int_{x=-2}^{2} (4 - x^2)\, dx$$

Note that we could have written down this single integral over x in the first step. We could have said that the area between the parabola and line equals the area under the line minus the area under the parabola:

$$A = A_{line} - A_{parabola} = \int_{x=-2}^{2} 4\, dx - \int_{x=-2}^{2} x^2\, dx$$

$$= 4[x]_{x=-2}^{2} - \left[\frac{x^3}{3}\right]_{x=-2}^{2} = 4[2 - (-2)] - \left[\frac{2^3}{3} - \frac{(-2)^3}{3}\right] = 4(2 + 2) - \left(\frac{8}{3} + \frac{8}{3}\right)$$

$$4(4) - \left(\frac{16}{3}\right) = 16 - \frac{16}{3} = \frac{48}{3} - \frac{16}{3} = \frac{48 - 16}{3} = \boxed{\frac{32}{3}} \approx \boxed{10.667}$$

Date: ________________ Name: ________________________________

Problem 26

Directions: Perform the following derivative.

$$\frac{d}{dx}(2^x x^2)$$

❖You can find the solution on the following page.

Solution to Problem 26

Apply the product rule with $f = 2^x$ and $g = x^2$:

$$\frac{d}{dx}(2^x x^2) = \frac{d}{dx}(fg) = g\frac{df}{dx} + f\frac{dg}{dx} = x^2\frac{d}{dx}2^x + 2^x\frac{d}{dx}x^2 = x^2\frac{d}{dx}2^x + 2^x(2x)$$

The identity $e^{\ln y} = y$ allows us to write $e^{\ln 2^x} = 2^x$. The identity $\ln p^q = q\ln p$ allows us to write $\ln 2^x = x\ln 2$. Substitute $\ln 2^x = x\ln 2$ into $e^{\ln 2^x} = 2^x$ to get $e^{x\ln 2} = 2^x$. The derivative $\frac{d}{dx}2^x$ becomes:

$$\frac{d}{dx}2^x = \frac{d}{dx}\left(e^{x\ln 2}\right)$$

Recall that $\frac{d}{dx}e^{ax} = ae^{ax}$. In our case, $a = \ln 2$.

$$\frac{d}{dx}\left(e^{x\ln 2}\right) = (\ln 2)e^{x\ln 2} = e^{x\ln 2}\ln 2$$

On the both the left-hand side and the right-hand side of the above equation, replace $e^{x\ln 2}$ with 2^x (since previously we showed that $e^{x\ln 2} = 2^x$).

$$\frac{d}{dx}2^x = (\ln 2)e^{x\ln 2} = 2^x\ln 2$$

We just found that $\frac{d}{dx}2^x = 2^x\ln 2$. Substitute this into the equation for $\frac{d}{dx}(2^x x^2)$ from near the beginning of our solution.

$$\frac{d}{dx}(2^x x^2) = x^2\frac{d}{dx}2^x + 2^x(2x) = x^2(2^x\ln 2) + 2^x(2x)$$

$$= \boxed{x^2 2^x\ln 2 + 2x2^x} = \boxed{2^x(x^2\ln 2 + 2x)} = \boxed{x2^x(x\ln 2 + 2)}$$

The last three expressions are all equivalent. The only difference is that the second and third equations have factored out something that is common to each term.

Date: ____________ Name: ______________________________

Problem 27

Directions: The rectangular block of cheese illustrated below on the left is sliced at an angle through the plane DFG. Perform a triple integral to find the volume of DFGH (shown below on the right) compared to the original volume of the rectangular block.

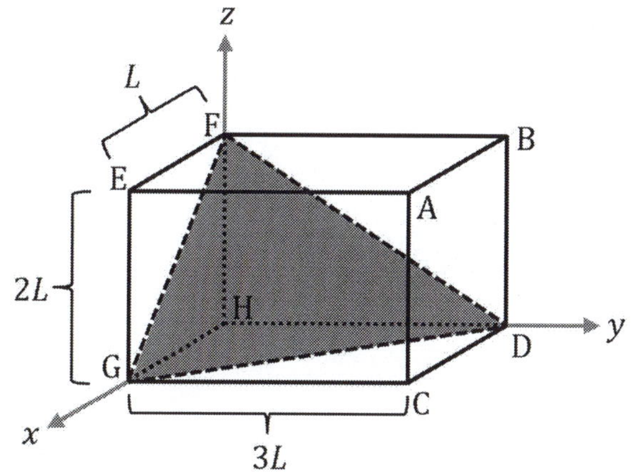

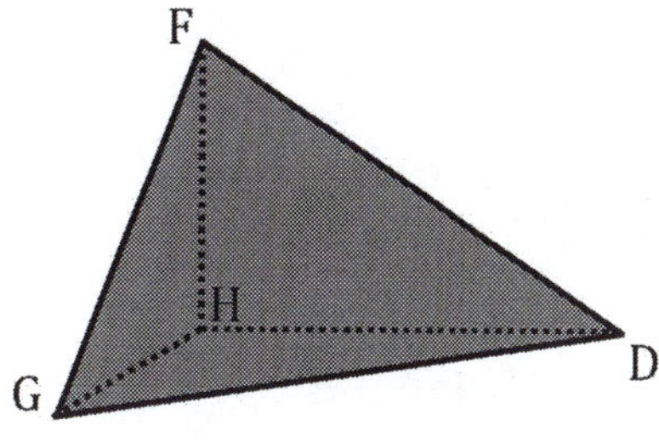

❖You can find the solution on the following page.

Solution to Problem 27

Let x vary from 0 to L. For a given value of x, the variable y can be no greater than $y = -3x + 3L$, which is the equation of the line DG (this line has slope $\frac{3L-0}{0-L} = -3$ and a y-intercept of $3L$). For given values of x and y, the variable z can be no greater than $z = -2x - \frac{2y}{3} + 2L$, which is the equation of the plane DFG (line FG has slope $\frac{2L-0}{0-L} = -2$, line DF has slope $\frac{2L-0}{0-3L} = -\frac{2}{3}$, and the z-intercept is $2L$).

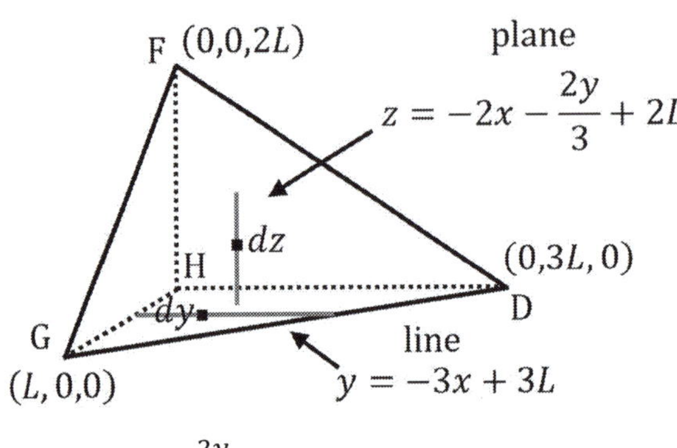

$$V = \int dV = \int_{x=0}^{L} \int_{y=0}^{-3x+3L} \int_{z=0}^{-2x-\frac{2y}{3}+2L} dz\, dy\, dx = \int_{x=0}^{L} \int_{y=0}^{-3x+3L} [z]_{z=0}^{-2x-\frac{2y}{3}+2L} dy\, dx$$

$$= \int_{x=0}^{L} \int_{y=0}^{-3x+3L} \left(-2x - \frac{2y}{3} + 2L\right) dy\, dx = \int_{x=0}^{L} \left[-2xy - \frac{y^2}{3} + 2Ly\right]_{y=0}^{-3x+3L} dx$$

$$= \int_{x=0}^{L} \left[-2x(-3x+3L) - \frac{(-3x+3L)^2}{3} + 2L(-3x+3L)\right] dx$$

$$= \int_{x=0}^{L} (6x^2 - 6Lx - 3x^2 + 6Lx - 3L^2 - 6Lx + 6L^2)\, dx$$

$$= \int_{x=0}^{L} (3x^2 - 6Lx + 3L^2)\, dx = [x^3 - 3Lx^2 + 3L^2x]_{x=0}^{L} = L^3 - 3L^3 + 3L^3 = L^3$$

The volume of the original block is $V_b = (L)(3L)(2L) = 6L^3$, such that $V = L^3 = \boxed{\frac{V_b}{6}}$. Our result, $V = L^3$, agrees with the geometric formula for the volume of an irregular tetrahedron, $V = \frac{1}{3}A_{base}h$, which for this case works out to $V = \frac{1}{3}\left[\frac{1}{2}(3L)(L)\right](2L) = L^3$.

Date: ____________________ Name: ____

Problem 28

Directions: A boy steals a monkey's banana and drives away in a golf cart (along a straight line). The monkey gives the boy a head start, and then chases the boy. The monkey and boy travel according to the following equations:

$$x_b = \frac{t_b^2}{12} \quad , \quad x_m = 3t_m$$

- t_b represents the time (in seconds) that the boy has been running.
- x_b represents the position (in meters) of the boy.
- t_m represents the time (in seconds) that the monkey has been running.
- x_m represents the position (in meters) of the monkey.

Apply calculus to determine the maximum head start (in seconds) that the monkey can give the boy such that the monkey is able to catch the boy.

❖You can find the solution on the following page.

Solution to Problem 28

Since the boy starts running first, the boy spends more time traveling, such that t_b is larger than t_m by the amount of the head start, h. (Many students write the following equation incorrectly. However, if you ask yourself who travels for the most amount of time, this helps to arrange the symbols in the equation correctly.)

$$t_b = t_m + h$$

When the monkey catches the boy, at that exact moment the boy and monkey will be in the same place, meaning that x_b will equal x_m. Set the given equations equal to each other.

$$x_b = x_m$$

$$\frac{t_b^2}{12} = 3t_m$$

Substitute $t_m = t_b - h$ (which comes from $t_b = t_m + h$) into the previous equation.

$$\frac{t_b^2}{12} = 3(t_b - h) = 3t_b - 3h$$

Isolate the head start, h. Add $3h$ to both sides and subtract $\frac{t_b^2}{12}$ from both sides.

$$3h = 3t_b - \frac{t_b^2}{12}$$

$$h = t_b - \frac{t_b^2}{36}$$

We want to find the maximum value of h. How do you find the extreme values of a function with calculus? Take a derivative of h with respect to t_b and set the derivative equal to zero:

$$\frac{dh}{dt_b} = \frac{d}{dt_b}\left(t_b - \frac{t_b^2}{36}\right) = \frac{d}{dt_b}t_b - \frac{d}{dt_b}\frac{t_b^2}{36} = 1 - \frac{t_b}{18} = 0$$

Solve for t_b.

$$1 - \frac{t_b}{18} = 0 \quad \to \quad 1 = \frac{t_b}{18} \quad \to \quad 18 = t_b$$

Plug $t_b = 18$ into the equation for the head start.

$$h = t_b - \frac{t_b^2}{36} = 18 - \frac{18^2}{36} = 18 - \frac{324}{36} = 18 - 9 = \boxed{9}$$

The monkey can afford to wait up to $h = 9$ seconds and still be able to catch the boy. (In calculus, problems like this are called "optimization problems.")

Date: ____________________ Name: ____

Problem 29

Directions: Perform the following integral.

$$\int_{x=0}^{\frac{5\sqrt{3}}{4}} \frac{dx}{(16x^2 + 25)^{3/2}}$$

❖You can find the solution on the following page.

Solution to Problem 29

Make the substitution $4x = 5\tan\theta$ in order to apply the identity $\tan^2\theta + 1 = \sec^2\theta$. Implicitly differentiate $4x = 5\tan\theta$ to get $4\,dx = 5\sec^2\theta\,d\theta$. (A derivative of $4x$ with respect to x equals 4, and a derivative of $5\tan\theta$ with respect to θ equals $5\sec^2\theta$.) Divide both sides of $4x = 5\tan\theta$ and $4\,dx = 5\sec^2\theta\,d\theta$ by 4 to get $x = \frac{5}{4}\tan\theta$ and $dx = \frac{5}{4}\sec^2\theta\,d\theta$. Solve for θ in $4x = 5\tan\theta$ to get $\theta = \tan^{-1}\left(\frac{4x}{5}\right)$ to determine the new limits of integration: $\theta_1 = \tan^{-1}(0) = 0$ and $\theta_2 = \tan^{-1}\left(\frac{4}{5}\frac{5\sqrt{3}}{4}\right) = \tan^{-1}(\sqrt{3}) = \frac{\pi}{3}$.

$$\int_{x=0}^{\frac{5\sqrt{3}}{4}} \frac{dx}{(16x^2+25)^{3/2}} = \int_{\theta=0}^{\pi/3} \frac{\frac{5}{4}\sec^2\theta\,d\theta}{\left[16\left(\frac{5}{4}\tan\theta\right)^2 + 25\right]^{3/2}}$$

Note that $\left(\frac{5}{4}\tan\theta\right)^2 = \frac{25}{16}\tan^2\theta$ because $(cx)^n = c^n x^n$.

$$\int_{\theta=0}^{\pi/3} \frac{\frac{5}{4}\sec^2\theta\,d\theta}{\left[16\left(\frac{5}{4}\tan\theta\right)^2 + 25\right]^{3/2}} = \frac{5}{4}\int_{\theta=0}^{\pi/3} \frac{\sec^2\theta\,d\theta}{\left[16\left(\frac{25}{16}\tan^2\theta\right) + 25\right]^{3/2}}$$

$$= \frac{5}{4}\int_{\theta=0}^{\pi/3} \frac{\sec^2\theta\,d\theta}{[25\tan^2\theta + 25]^{3/2}} = \frac{5}{4}\int_{\theta=0}^{\pi/3} \frac{\sec^2\theta\,d\theta}{[25(\tan^2\theta + 1)]^{3/2}}$$

$$= \frac{5}{4}\int_{\theta=0}^{\pi/3} \frac{\sec^2\theta\,d\theta}{(25)^{3/2}(\tan^2\theta + 1)^{3/2}} = \frac{5}{4}\int_{\theta=0}^{\pi/3} \frac{\sec^2\theta\,d\theta}{125\sec^3\theta} = \frac{5}{500}\int_{\theta=0}^{\pi/3} \frac{d\theta}{\sec\theta}$$

$$= \frac{1}{100}\int_{\theta=0}^{\pi/3} \cos\theta\,d\theta = \frac{1}{100}[\sin\theta]_{\theta=0}^{\frac{\pi}{3}} = \frac{1}{100}\left[\sin\left(\frac{\pi}{3}\right) - \sin 0\right]$$

$$= \frac{1}{100}\left(\frac{\sqrt{3}}{2} - 0\right) = \boxed{\frac{\sqrt{3}}{200}} \approx \boxed{0.00866}$$

Note that $\tan^2\theta + 1 = \sec^2\theta$ and that $\frac{1}{\sec\theta} = \cos\theta$ since $\sec\theta = \frac{1}{\cos\theta}$. Also note that $25^{3/2} = 25^{1+1/2} = 25^1 25^{1/2} = 25\sqrt{25} = 25(5) = 125$ and $\sin\left(\frac{\pi}{3}\right) = \sin(60°) = \frac{\sqrt{3}}{2}$.

Date: ________________ Name: ______________________________

Problem 30

Directions: Evaluate the following derivative at $x = 64$.

$$\frac{d}{dx}\left(\frac{x^{3/2}}{4} - \frac{448}{x^{1/3}}\right)^{7/4}$$

❖You can find the solution on the following page.

Solution to Problem 30

This is an application of the chain rule, involving inside and outside functions. After you take a derivative of the outside function, you then take a derivative of the inside function. Note that $\frac{1}{x^{1/3}} = x^{-1/3}$ according to the rule $x^{-n} = \frac{1}{x^n}$.

- The outside function is $f(u) = u^{7/4}$.
- The inside function is $u(x) = \frac{x^{3/2}}{4} - \frac{448}{x^{1/3}} = \frac{x^{3/2}}{4} - 448x^{-1/3}$.

According to the chain rule, we multiply the two derivatives together:

$$\frac{df}{dx} = \frac{df}{du}\frac{du}{dx} = \left(\frac{d}{du}u^{7/4}\right)\left[\frac{d}{dx}\left(\frac{x^{3/2}}{4} - 448x^{-1/3}\right)\right] = \frac{7}{4}u^{3/4}\left(\frac{d}{dx}\frac{x^{3/2}}{4} - \frac{d}{dx}448x^{-1/3}\right)$$

$$= \frac{7}{4}u^{3/4}\left(\frac{3}{8}x^{1/2} + \frac{448}{3}x^{-4/3}\right) = \frac{7}{4}\left(\frac{x^{3/2}}{4} - \frac{448}{x^{1/3}}\right)^{3/4}\left(\frac{3}{8}x^{1/2} + \frac{448}{3x^{4/3}}\right)$$

Evaluate this derivative at $x = 64$:

$$\left.\frac{df}{dx}\right|_{x=64} = \frac{7}{4}\left(\frac{64^{3/2}}{4} - \frac{448}{64^{1/3}}\right)^{3/4}\left[\frac{3}{8}(64)^{1/2} + \frac{448}{3(64)^{4/3}}\right]$$

$$= \frac{7}{4}\left(\frac{512}{4} - \frac{448}{4}\right)^{3/4}\left[\frac{3}{8}(8) + \frac{448}{3(256)}\right] = \frac{7}{4}(128 - 112)^{3/4}\left[\frac{3}{8}(8) + \frac{448}{768}\right]$$

$$= \frac{7}{4}(16)^{3/4}\left(3 + \frac{448}{768}\right) = \frac{7}{4}(8)\left(\frac{2304}{768} + \frac{448}{768}\right) = \frac{56}{4}\left(\frac{2752}{768}\right)$$

$$= 14\left(\frac{2752}{768}\right) = \frac{38{,}528}{768} = \boxed{\frac{301}{6}} \approx \boxed{50.167}$$

Note that $64^{3/2} = \left(64^{1/2}\right)^3 = \left(\sqrt{64}\right)^3 = 8^3 = 512$, $64^{4/3} = \left(64^{1/3}\right)^4 = \left(\sqrt[3]{64}\right)^4 = 4^4 = 256$, and $16^{3/4} = \left(16^{1/4}\right)^3 = 2^3 = 8$ according to the rule $x^{mn} = (x^m)^n = (x^n)^m$. Reduce $\frac{38{,}528}{768}$ to $\frac{301}{6}$ by dividing 38,528 and 768 each by their greatest common factor (which is 128): $\frac{38{,}528}{768} = \frac{38{,}528 \div 128}{768 \div 128} = \frac{301}{6}$.

Date: ____________ Name: ______________________________

Problem 31

Directions: Illustrated below is the graph of a simple spiral given by the equation $r = \theta$. Determine the area between the first $(0 \leq \theta \leq 2\pi)$ and second $(2\pi \leq \theta \leq 4\pi)$ windings of the spiral.

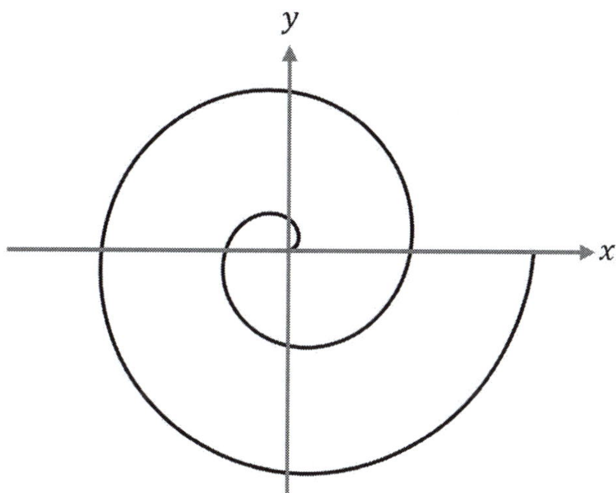

❖You can find the solution on the following page.

Solution to Problem 31

Area can be expressed as a double integral. This problem is simpler if we choose to work with the 2D polar coordinates r and θ. In 2D polar coordinates, the differential area element is $dA = rdrd\theta$. (It is a common mistake for students to write $drd\theta$ instead of $rdrd\theta$. However, area is measured in square meters: $drd\theta$ can't possibly be area because it has units of meters. Note that $dA = rdrd\theta$ correctly has units of square meters.) The equation for the curve is $r = \theta$ (this was given in the problem). The variable θ varies from 2π to 4π for the second winding.

The limits of r can be a little 'tricky' in this problem. The lower limit of r equals $\theta - 2\pi$ and the upper limit of r equals θ. Why? Because we want to integrate radially outward from the first winding to the second winding (to properly subtract out the area of the first winding). For any value of θ, since $r = \theta$ is the equation of the spiral, as θ varies from 2π to 4π, the value of r for the first winding is exactly 2π less than the value of r for the second winding. Subtract 2π from θ to get $\theta - 2\pi$.

We must integrate over r first because its limits involve the variable θ.

$$A = \int dA = \int_{\theta=2\pi}^{4\pi} \int_{r=\theta-2\pi}^{\theta} r\, dr\, d\theta = \int_{\theta=2\pi}^{4\pi} \left[\frac{r^2}{2}\right]_{r=\theta-2\pi}^{\theta} d\theta$$

$$A = \int_{\theta=2\pi}^{4\pi} \left(\frac{\theta^2}{2} - \frac{(\theta-2\pi)^2}{2}\right) d\theta = \int_{\theta=2\pi}^{4\pi} \left(\frac{\theta^2}{2} - \frac{\theta^2 - 4\pi\theta + 4\pi^2}{2}\right) d\theta$$

$$A = \int_{\theta=2\pi}^{4\pi} \left(\frac{\theta^2}{2} + \frac{-\theta^2 + 4\pi\theta - 4\pi^2}{2}\right) d\theta = \int_{\theta=2\pi}^{4\pi} (2\pi\theta - 2\pi^2)\, d\theta$$

$$A = [\pi\theta^2 - 2\pi^2\theta]_{\theta=2\pi}^{4\pi} = \pi(4\pi)^2 - 2\pi^2(4\pi) - [\pi(2\pi)^2 - 2\pi^2(2\pi)]$$

$$A = 16\pi^3 - 8\pi^3 - (4\pi^3 - 4\pi^3) = 16\pi^3 - 8\pi^3 - 0 = \boxed{8\pi^3} \approx \boxed{248.05}$$

Note that $(4\pi)^3 = 64\pi^3$ and $(2\pi)^3 = 8\pi^3$ according to the rule $(ax)^n = a^n x^n$. Be careful distributing the minus signs.

Check the answer: There is a simple way to check that the answer makes sense. For the first winding, r varies from 0 to 2π with an average value of π. The area of the first winding is approximately equal to the area of a circle with a radius of π, which is $A_1 \approx \pi(\pi)^2 = \pi^3$. For the second winding, r varies from 2π to 4π with an average value of 3π. The area of the second winding is approximately equal to the area of a circle with a radius of 3π, which is $A_2 \approx \pi(3\pi)^2 = 9\pi^3$. To get an approximation for the area between the two windings, subtract these areas: $A_2 - A_1 \approx 9\pi^3 - \pi^3 = 8\pi^3$. (It's not just an approximation; it's exact. Why? Because the equation for the spiral, $r = \theta$, is linear.)

Date: ____________ Name: ______________________________

Problem 32

Directions: Evaluate the following limit.

$$\lim_{x \to 0} \frac{1 - e^{-x/2}}{\ln(x + 1)}$$

❖You can find the solution on the following page.

Solution to Problem 32

The limit doesn't equal zero, even though the numerator, $1 - e^{-x/2}$, approaches zero in the limit that x approaches zero. Why not? The denominator, $\ln(x+1)$, also approaches zero in the limit that x approaches zero (since $\ln 1 = 0$). Recall from arithmetic that the fraction $0/0$ is indeterminate. This limit can be evaluated by applying l'Hôpital's rule, which involves taking derivatives of both the numerator and denominator.

$$\lim_{x\to 0}\frac{1-e^{-x/2}}{\ln(x+1)} = \frac{\frac{d}{dx}\left[1-e^{-x/2}\right]_{x=0}}{\frac{d}{dx}\left[\ln(x+1)\right]_{x=0}} = \frac{\left[\frac{d}{dx}(1)-\frac{d}{dx}\left(e^{-x/2}\right)\right]_{x=0}}{\frac{d}{dx}\left[\ln(x+1)\right]_{x=0}}$$

Recall that $\frac{d}{dx}e^{ax} = ae^{ax}$ (note that $a = -\frac{1}{2}$) and $\frac{d}{dx}\ln(x+1) = \frac{1}{x+1}$.

$$\lim_{x\to 0}\frac{1-e^{-x/2}}{\ln(x+1)} = \frac{\left[0-\left(-\frac{1}{2}\right)e^{-x/2}\right]_{x=0}}{\left[\frac{1}{x+1}\right]_{x=0}} = \frac{\left[\frac{1}{2}e^{-x/2}\right]_{x=0}}{\frac{1}{0+1}} = \frac{\frac{1}{2}e^{-0/2}}{\frac{1}{1}}$$

$$= \frac{\frac{1}{2}e^{0}}{1} = \frac{\frac{1}{2}(1)}{1} = \frac{1/2}{1} = \boxed{\frac{1}{2}} = \boxed{0.5}$$

Note that $e^0 = 1$.

Date: ____________ Name: ______________________

Problem 33

Directions: Perform the following fifteenth derivative.

$$\frac{d^{15}}{dx^{15}}\frac{(3-2x)^{18}}{14!\,2^{16}}$$

Note that $n!$ (read as n factorial) means $n! = n(n-1)(n-2)\cdots(3)(2)(1)$, meaning to multiply n by all of the integers less than n until you reach the number 1. Also note that 2 is raised to the power of 16 in the denominator. The fifteenth derivative is similar to a second derivative, except that it involves taking additional derivatives.

❖You can find the solution on the following page.

Solution to Problem 33

We need to take fifteen consecutive derivatives of the given expression. Begin by taking the first derivative, which involves applying the chain rule with an outside function, $f(u) = \frac{u^{18}}{14!2^{16}}$ and an inside function, $u(x) = 3 - 2x$, where 14! and 2^{16} are constants.

$$\frac{d}{dx}\frac{(3-2x)^{18}}{14!\,2^{16}} = \frac{1}{14!\,2^{16}}\frac{d}{dx}(3-2x)^{18} = \frac{1}{14!\,2^{16}}\frac{df}{dx} = \frac{1}{14!\,2^{16}}\frac{df}{du}\frac{du}{dx}$$

$$= \left(\frac{d}{du}\frac{u^{18}}{14!\,2^{16}}\right)\left[\frac{d}{dx}(3-2x)\right] = \frac{1}{14!\,2^{16}}\left(\frac{d}{du}u^{18}\right)\left[\frac{d}{dx}(3-2x)\right]$$

$$= \frac{1}{14!\,2^{16}}(18u^{17})(-2) = -\frac{(18)(2)u^{17}}{14!\,2^{16}} = -\frac{(18)(2)(3-2x)^{17}}{14!\,2^{16}} = -\frac{(18)(3-2x)^{17}}{14!\,2^{15}}$$

Let's work out the first few derivatives in order to help see what pattern emerges.

$$\frac{d}{dx}\frac{(3-2x)^{18}}{14!\,2^{16}} = -\frac{(18)(3-2x)^{17}}{14!\,2^{15}}$$

$$\frac{d^2}{dx^2}\frac{(3-2x)^{18}}{14!\,2^{16}} = \frac{d}{dx}\left[-\frac{(18)(3-2x)^{17}}{14!\,2^{15}}\right] = \frac{(18)(17)(3-2x)^{16}}{14!\,2^{14}}$$

$$\frac{d^3}{dx^3}\frac{(3-2x)^{18}}{14!\,2^{16}} = \frac{d}{dx}\frac{(18)(17)(3-2x)^{16}}{14!\,2^{14}} = -\frac{(18)(17)(16)(3-2x)^{15}}{14!\,2^{13}}$$

$$\frac{d^4}{dx^4}\frac{(3-2x)^{18}}{14!\,2^{16}} = \frac{d}{dx}\left[-\frac{(18)(17)(16)(3-2x)^{15}}{14!\,2^{13}}\right] = \frac{(18)(17)(16)(15)(3-2x)^{14}}{14!\,2^{12}}$$

- From the chain rule, each time that we take a derivative, a factor of (-2) appears from the derivative of the inside function, since $\frac{d}{dx}(3-2x) = -2$.
- Each derivative brings down the previous exponent and reduces the exponent by one. We get $(18)(17)(16)\cdots$, and the exponent will be reduced by n.

What will happen with the fifteenth derivative?

- $(-2)^{15} = -2^{15}$ will come out from applying the chain rule 15 times.
- The 15th derivative will have $(18)(17)(16)\cdots(6)(5)(4)$ out front. $18 - 15 = 3$, yet the 15th factor is actually 4, which is 1 higher than 3. If you read pages 4-6 in a book, you actually read 3 pages (4, 5, and 6) even though $6 - 4 = 2$.

$$\frac{d^{15}}{dx^{15}}\frac{(3-2x)^{18}}{14!\,2^{16}} = \frac{(18)(17)(16)\cdots(6)(5)(4)(-2^{15})(3-2x)^3}{14!\,2^{16}}$$

Note that $(14)(13)(12)\cdots(6)(5)(4)$ from the top cancels all but $(3)(2)(1)$ of 14!.

$$-\frac{(18)(17)(16)(15)}{(3)(2)(1)}\frac{2^{15}}{2^{16}}(3-2x)^3 = -12{,}240\left(\frac{1}{2}\right)(3-2x)^3$$

$$= \boxed{-6120(3-2x)^3} = \boxed{6120(2x-3)^3}$$

Date: ____________________ Name: ____

Problem 34

Directions: Perform the following integral.

$$\int_{x=4}^{7} \frac{dx}{\sqrt{x^2 - 8x + 25}}$$

❖You can find the solution on the following page.

Solution to Problem 34

Note that $(x-4)^2 = (x-4)(x-4) = x^2 - 8x + 16$. Since $25 = 16 + 9$, we can write $x^2 - 8x + 25 = x^2 - 8x + 16 + 9 = (x^2 - 8x + 16) + 9 = (x-4)(x-4) + 9$. (This is called "completing the square.")

$$\int_{x=4}^{7} \frac{dx}{\sqrt{x^2 - 8x + 25}} = \int_{x=4}^{7} \frac{dx}{\sqrt{(x-4)(x-4)+9}} = \int_{x=4}^{7} \frac{dx}{\sqrt{(x-4)^2+9}}$$

Make the substitution $x - 4 = 3\tan\theta$. Implicitly differentiate $x - 4 = 3\tan\theta$ to get $dx = 3\sec^2\theta\, d\theta$ (the derivative of tangent is secant squared). Divide both sides of $x - 4 = 3\tan\theta$ by 3 to get $\frac{x-4}{3} = \tan\theta$. The new limits of integration are:

$$\theta_1 = \tan^{-1}\left(\frac{4-4}{3}\right) = \tan^{-1}(0) = 0 \quad , \quad \theta_2 = \tan^{-1}\left(\frac{7-4}{3}\right) = \tan^{-1}(1) = \frac{\pi}{4}$$

With the substitution $x - 4 = 3\tan\theta$, the integral becomes:

$$\int_{x=4}^{7} \frac{dx}{\sqrt{(x-4)^2+9}} = \int_{\theta=0}^{\pi/4} \frac{3\sec^2\theta\, d\theta}{\sqrt{(3\tan\theta)^2+9}} = \int_{\theta=0}^{\pi/4} \frac{3\sec^2\theta\, d\theta}{\sqrt{9\tan^2\theta+9}}$$

Note that $(3\tan\theta)^2 = 9\tan^2\theta$ because $(cx)^n = c^n x^n$.

$$\int_{\theta=0}^{\pi/4} \frac{3\sec^2\theta\, d\theta}{\sqrt{9\tan^2\theta+9}} = \int_{\theta=0}^{\pi/4} \frac{3\sec^2\theta\, d\theta}{\sqrt{9(\tan^2\theta+1)}} = \int_{\theta=0}^{\pi/4} \frac{3\sec^2\theta\, d\theta}{\sqrt{9(\sec^2\theta)}} = \int_{\theta=0}^{\pi/4} \frac{3\sec^2\theta\, d\theta}{3\sec\theta}$$

Recall the trig identity $\tan^2\theta + 1 = \sec^2\theta$.

$$\int_{\theta=0}^{\pi/4} \frac{3\sec^2\theta\, d\theta}{3\sec\theta} = \int_{\theta=0}^{\pi/4} \frac{\sec^2\theta\, d\theta}{\sec\theta} = \int_{\theta=0}^{\pi/4} \sec\theta\, d\theta = [\ln|\sec\theta + \tan\theta|]_{\theta=0}^{\pi/4}$$

$$= \ln\left|\sec\left(\frac{\pi}{4}\right) + \tan\left(\frac{\pi}{4}\right)\right| - \ln|\sec(0) + \tan(0)| = \ln\left|\sqrt{2} + 1\right| - \ln|1 + 0|$$

$$= \ln\left(\sqrt{2}+1\right) - \ln(1) = \ln\left(\sqrt{2}+1\right) - 0 = \boxed{\ln\left(\sqrt{2}+1\right)} \approx \boxed{0.881}$$

Note that $\frac{3}{\sqrt{3}} = \sqrt{3}$ because $\sqrt{3}\sqrt{3} = 3$ and that $\ln(1) = 0$. Also note that $\frac{\pi}{4}$rad $= 45°$, $\sec 45° = \frac{1}{\cos 45°} = \sqrt{2}$, and $\tan 45° = 1$. An alternative method of solving this problem leads to $\sinh^{-1}(1) = 0.881$, where sinh is a hyperbolic function (not the ordinary trig function), which is identical to our answer.

Date: ____________________ Name: ____

Problem 35

Directions: An object travels with one-dimensional motion. The object's acceleration, $a = \frac{dv}{dt} = \frac{d^2x}{dt^2}$, is given by the equation $a = \frac{k}{\sqrt{x}}$, where $k = 3$ (in units of $\frac{\text{m}^{3/2}}{\text{s}^2}$). The object starts at $x = 9$ m with an initial velocity of $v = 4$ m/s. Determine the object's velocity when it reaches $x = 16$ m.

❖You can find the solution on the following page.

Solution to Problem 35

Plug $a = \frac{k}{\sqrt{x}}$ into the equation $a = \frac{dv}{dt}$.

$$\frac{k}{\sqrt{x}} = \frac{dv}{dt}$$

We can't integrate yet because there are three variables: x, v, and t. The trick is to apply the chain rule and to note that velocity is a derivative of position with respect to time $\left(v = \frac{dx}{dt}\right)$:

$$\frac{dv}{dt} = \frac{dv}{dx}\frac{dx}{dt} = \left(\frac{dv}{dx}\right)(v) = v\frac{dv}{dx}$$

Replace $\frac{dv}{dt}$ with $v\frac{dv}{dx}$ in the equation $\frac{k}{\sqrt{x}} = \frac{dv}{dt}$.

$$\frac{k}{\sqrt{x}} = v\frac{dv}{dx}$$

Separate variables. This means to put only x on one side of the equation and only v on the other side of the equation. Multiply both sides of the equation by dx.

$$\frac{k}{\sqrt{x}}dx = v\,dv$$

Now that we have just two variables with each variable on its own side of the equation, we may integrate both sides. We will call the constant of integration c.

$$k\int\frac{dx}{\sqrt{x}} = \int v\,dv$$

$$2k\sqrt{x} = \frac{v^2}{2} + c$$

Note that $\int\frac{dx}{\sqrt{x}} = \int\frac{dx}{x^{1/2}} = \int x^{-1/2}\,dx = \frac{x^{-1/2+1}}{-\frac{1}{2}+1} = \frac{x^{1/2}}{1/2} = 2x^{1/2} = 2\sqrt{x}$. According to the problem, $v = 4$ m/s when $x = 9$ m. Also note that $k = 3$. Use these numbers to find c.

$$2(3)\sqrt{9} = \frac{4^2}{2} + c \quad \to \quad 18 = 8 + c \quad \to \quad 18 - 8 = 10 = c$$

Now plug in $c = 10$ (by the way, its units happen to be $\frac{\text{m}^2}{\text{s}^2}$) and $x = 16$ m.

$$2(3)\sqrt{16} = \frac{v^2}{2} + 10 \quad \to \quad 24 = \frac{v^2}{2} + 10 \quad \to \quad 14 = \frac{v^2}{2} \quad \to \quad \sqrt{28} = 2\sqrt{7} = v$$

The velocity is $v = \boxed{2\sqrt{7}} \approx \boxed{5.3}$ m/s when $x = 16$ m. Observe that $\sqrt{28} = \sqrt{(4)(7)} = \sqrt{4}\sqrt{7} = 2\sqrt{7}$.

Date: ____________________ Name: ____

Problem 36

Directions: Perform the following derivative, where $x > 1$.

$$\frac{d}{dx}\sqrt{\sqrt{x} - \frac{1}{\sqrt{x}}}$$

❖You can find the solution on the following page.

Solution to Problem 36

Apply the chain rule, with $f(u) = \sqrt{u} = u^{1/2}$ and $u(x) = \sqrt{x} - \frac{1}{\sqrt{x}}$.

$$\frac{d}{dx}\sqrt{\sqrt{x} - \frac{1}{\sqrt{x}}} = \frac{df}{dx} = \frac{df}{du}\frac{du}{dx} = \left(\frac{d}{du}u^{1/2}\right)\left[\frac{d}{dx}\left(\sqrt{x} - \frac{1}{\sqrt{x}}\right)\right]$$

$$= \left(\frac{1}{2}u^{-1/2}\right)\left[\frac{d}{dx}\sqrt{x} - \frac{d}{dx}\left(\frac{1}{\sqrt{x}}\right)\right] = \frac{1}{2u^{1/2}}\left[\frac{d}{dx}x^{1/2} - \frac{d}{dx}\left(\frac{1}{x^{1/2}}\right)\right]$$

$$= \frac{1}{2\sqrt{\sqrt{x} - \frac{1}{\sqrt{x}}}}\left[\frac{1}{2}x^{-1/2} - \frac{d}{dx}\left(x^{-1/2}\right)\right] = \frac{1}{2\sqrt{\sqrt{x}\frac{\sqrt{x}}{\sqrt{x}} - \frac{1}{\sqrt{x}}}}\left[\frac{1}{2}x^{-1/2} - \left(-\frac{1}{2}\right)x^{-3/2}\right]$$

$$= \frac{1}{2\sqrt{\frac{x}{\sqrt{x}} - \frac{1}{\sqrt{x}}}}\left(\frac{1}{2}x^{-1/2} + \frac{1}{2}x^{-3/2}\right) = \frac{1}{2\sqrt{\frac{x-1}{\sqrt{x}}}}\left(\frac{1}{2x^{1/2}} + \frac{1}{2x^{3/2}}\right)$$

$$= \frac{1}{2}\sqrt{\frac{\sqrt{x}}{x-1}}\left(\frac{1}{2\sqrt{x}} + \frac{1}{2x\sqrt{x}}\right) = \frac{\sqrt{\sqrt{x}}}{2\sqrt{x-1}}\left(\frac{1}{2\sqrt{x}} + \frac{1}{2x\sqrt{x}}\right)$$

To divide by a fraction, multiply by its reciprocal. The reciprocal of $\frac{x-1}{\sqrt{x}}$ is $\frac{\sqrt{x}}{x-1}$. Note that $x^{3/2} = x^1 x^{1/2} = x\sqrt{x}$. In the next step, we will factor out $\frac{1}{2\sqrt{x}}$.

$$\frac{\sqrt{\sqrt{x}}}{2\sqrt{x-1}}\left(\frac{1}{2\sqrt{x}} + \frac{1}{2x\sqrt{x}}\right) = \frac{\sqrt{x^{1/2}}}{2\sqrt{x-1}}\left(\frac{1}{2\sqrt{x}}\right)\left(1 + \frac{1}{x}\right) = \frac{x^{1/4}}{4\sqrt{x}\sqrt{x-1}}\left(1 + \frac{1}{x}\right)$$

$$= \frac{x^{1/4}}{4x^{1/2}\sqrt{x-1}}\left(\frac{x}{x} + \frac{1}{x}\right) = \frac{1}{4x^{1/2-1/4}\sqrt{x-1}}\left(\frac{x+1}{x}\right) = \frac{1}{4x^{1/4}\sqrt{x-1}}\left(\frac{x+1}{x}\right)$$

$$= \frac{(x+1)}{4x^{1/4}x\sqrt{x-1}} = \frac{(x+1)}{4x^{1/4+1}\sqrt{x-1}} = \boxed{\frac{(x+1)}{4x^{5/4}\sqrt{x-1}}}$$

Note that $\frac{x^{1/4}}{x^{1/2}} = x^{1/4-1/2} = x^{-1/2}$ since $\frac{x^m}{x^n} = x^{m-n}$ and $\frac{1}{4} - \frac{1}{2} = -\frac{1}{4}$. Similarly, $x^{1/4}x^1 = x^{1/4+1} = x^{5/4}$. Note that if you wish to rationalize this denominator, you must not only multiply by $\frac{\sqrt{x-1}}{\sqrt{x-1}}$, but must also multiply by $\frac{x^{3/4}}{x^{3/4}}$. In that case, you get $\frac{(x+1)x^{3/4}\sqrt{x-1}}{4x^2(x-1)}$ since $x^{5/4}x^{3/4} = x^{5/4+3/4} = x^{8/4} = x^2$.

Date: ____________ Name: ______________________________

Problem 37

Directions: Perform the following integral.

$$\int_{\theta=\pi/6}^{\pi/3} \sec^4 \theta \, d\theta$$

❖ You can find the solution on the following page.

Solution to Problem 37

Apply the trig identity $\tan^2\theta + 1 = \sec^2\theta$.

$$\int_{\theta=\pi/6}^{\pi/3} \sec^4\theta\, d\theta = \int_{\theta=\pi/6}^{\pi/3} \sec^2\theta \sec^2\theta\, d\theta = \int_{\theta=\pi/6}^{\pi/3} (\tan^2\theta + 1)\sec^2\theta\, d\theta$$

$$= \int_{\theta=\pi/6}^{\pi/3} \tan^2\theta \sec^2\theta\, d\theta + \int_{\theta=\pi/6}^{\pi/3} \sec^2\theta\, d\theta$$

Make the substitution $u = \tan\theta$, such that $du = \sec^2\theta\, d\theta$ (since $\frac{d}{d\theta}\tan\theta = \sec^2\theta\, d\theta$). Use $u = \tan\theta$ to determine that the new limits are $u_1 = \tan\left(\frac{\pi}{6}\right) = \tan 30° = \frac{\sqrt{3}}{3}$ and $u_2 = \tan\left(\frac{\pi}{3}\right) = \tan 60° = \sqrt{3}$. (Note that $\frac{\sqrt{3}}{3}$ is the same as $\frac{1}{\sqrt{3}}$ since $\frac{1}{\sqrt{3}}\frac{\sqrt{3}}{\sqrt{3}} = \frac{\sqrt{3}}{3}$.) Substitute $u = \tan\theta$ and $du = \sec^2\theta\, d\theta$ into the integral.

$$\int_{\theta=\pi/6}^{\pi/3} \tan^2\theta \sec^2\theta\, d\theta + \int_{\theta=\pi/6}^{\pi/3} \sec^2\theta\, d\theta = \int_{u=\sqrt{3}/3}^{\sqrt{3}} u^2\, du + \int_{\theta=\sqrt{3}/3}^{\sqrt{3}} du$$

$$\left[\frac{u^3}{3}\right]_{u=\sqrt{3}/3}^{\sqrt{3}} + [u]_{u=\sqrt{3}/3}^{\sqrt{3}} = \frac{1}{3}[u^3]_{u=\sqrt{3}/3}^{\sqrt{3}} + [u]_{u=\sqrt{3}/3}^{\sqrt{3}}$$

$$= \frac{1}{3}\left(\sqrt{3}\right)^3 - \frac{1}{3}\left(\frac{\sqrt{3}}{3}\right)^3 + \sqrt{3} - \frac{\sqrt{3}}{3} = \frac{1}{3}\left(3\sqrt{3}\right) - \frac{1}{3}\left(\frac{3\sqrt{3}}{27}\right) + \sqrt{3} - \frac{\sqrt{3}}{3}$$

$$= \sqrt{3} - \frac{3\sqrt{3}}{81} + \sqrt{3} - \frac{\sqrt{3}}{3} = \sqrt{3} - \frac{\sqrt{3}}{27} + \sqrt{3} - \frac{\sqrt{3}}{3} = \frac{27\sqrt{3}}{27} - \frac{\sqrt{3}}{27} + \frac{27\sqrt{3}}{27} - \frac{9\sqrt{3}}{27}$$

$$= \frac{27\sqrt{3} - \sqrt{3} + 27\sqrt{3} - 9\sqrt{3}}{27} = \frac{(27 - 1 + 27 - 9)\sqrt{3}}{27} = \boxed{\frac{44\sqrt{3}}{27}} \approx \boxed{2.823}$$

Note that $\left(\sqrt{3}\right)^3 = \sqrt{3}\sqrt{3}\sqrt{3} = \left(\sqrt{3}\right)^2\sqrt{3} = 3\sqrt{3}$.

Date: ____________ Name: ______________________

Problem 38

Directions: The velocity, $v(t)$, of an object is graphed below as a function of time.

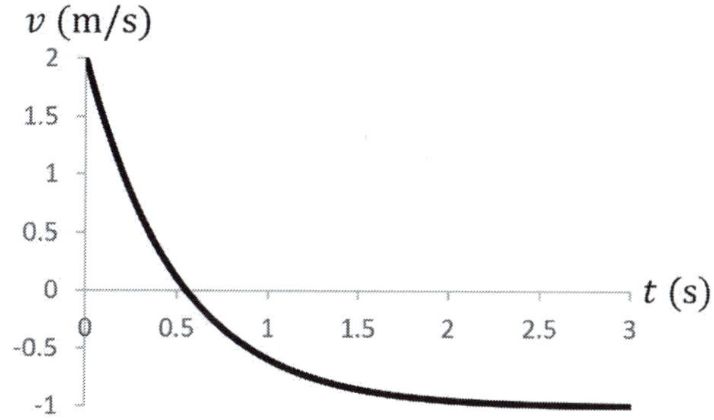

(A) Evaluate the acceleration, $a = \frac{dv}{dt}$, when $t = 1.0$ sec.

(B) Determine the displacement, $x = \int_{t=0}^{3} v\,dt$ (which tells where the object ended up at $t = 3$ sec relative to its starting point at $t = 0$ sec).

❖You can find the solution on the following page.

Solution to Problem 38

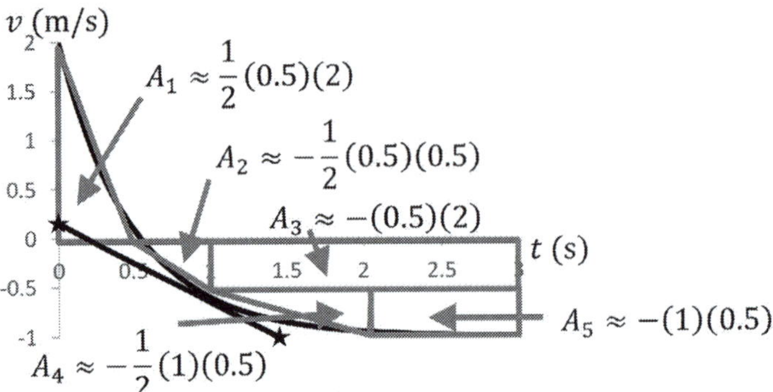

(A) Acceleration is the derivative of velocity with respect to time: $a = \frac{dv}{dt}$. How do you find the derivative from a graph? Find the slope of the tangent line at $t = 1.0$ sec. We drew a tangent line on the graph above. The approximate coordinates of the two ★'s are $(0, 0.15)$ and $(1.45, -1)$. If you drew your tangent line somewhat differently, your answer may be a bit off compared to our answer. (You can find the exact answer at the end of our solution.)

$$a = \frac{v_2 - v_1}{t_2 - t_1} = \frac{-1 - 0.15}{1.45 - 0} = \frac{-1.15}{1.45} \approx \boxed{-0.79 \text{ m/s}^2}$$

(B) Displacement is the integral of velocity over time: $x = \int v\, dt$. How do you find the integral from a graph? Find the area between the curve and the horizontal axis. We divided this area (approximately) into 3 triangles and 2 rectangles on the graph above. The initial area is positive, whereas area becomes negative when the curve dips below the time axis. Recall that the area of a triangle is $\frac{1}{2}BH$ and the area of a rectangle is WH. Depending on how you draw your shapes and interpolate, your area could be a bit off.

$$x = \text{area} \approx \frac{1}{2}(0.5)(2) - \frac{1}{2}(0.5)(0.5) - (0.5)(2) - \frac{1}{2}(1)(0.5) - (1)(0.5)$$

$$x \approx 0.5 - 0.125 - 1 - 0.25 - 0.5 \approx \boxed{-1.4 \text{ m}} \text{ (or 1.4 m behind where it started)}$$

Exact answers: You don't need to know that the actual function is $v = 3e^{-2t} - 1$ in order to solve this problem. However, in case you are skeptical about our solution, you can use it to see that $a = \frac{dv}{dt} = \frac{d}{dt}(3e^{-2t} - 1) = -6e^{-2t}$, $a(1) = -\frac{6}{e^2} \approx 0.81 \text{ m/s}^2$, and $x = \int v\, dt = \int_{t=0}^{3}(3e^{-2t} - 1)\, dt = \left[-\frac{3}{2}e^{-2t} - t\right]_{t=0}^{3} \approx -\frac{3}{2}e^{-6} - 3 + \frac{3}{2}e^0 + 0 \approx -0.0037 - 3 + 1.5 \approx -1.5$ m. Note that $\frac{3}{2}e^0 = \frac{3}{2}(1) = \frac{3}{2} = 1.5$.

Date: ________________ Name: ________________________________

Problem 39

Directions: Perform the following integral, given that $x > 2$.

$$\int \frac{9x + 2}{x^2 + x - 6} dx$$

❖You can find the solution on the following page.

Solution to Problem 39

Note that the denominator can be factored as $x^2 + x - 6 = (x + 3)(x - 2)$ because $(x + 3)(x - 2) = x^2 - 2x + 3x - 6 = x^2 + x - 6$. Use the method of partial fractions to rewrite the integrand as:

$$\frac{9x + 2}{(x + 3)(x - 2)} = \frac{A}{x + 3} + \frac{B}{x - 2}$$

Multiply both sides of the equation by $(x + 3)(x - 2)$.

$$9x + 2 = A(x - 2) + B(x + 3)$$

$$9x + 2 = Ax - 2A + Bx + 3B$$

$$9x + 2 = (A + B)x + 3B - 2A$$

Equate the coefficient of x on both sides of the equation, and equate the constant terms:

$$9 = A + B \quad , \quad 2 = 3B - 2A$$

Solve this system of equations. From the first equation, $B = 9 - A$. Plug this into the second equation: $2 = 3(9 - A) - 2A = 27 - 3A - 2A = 27 - 5A$. Add $5A$ to both sides of $2 = 27 - 5A$ to get $5A + 2 = 27$. Subtract 2 from both sides to get $5A = 25$. Divide both sides by 5 to get $A = \frac{25}{5} = 5$. Plug $A = 5$ into $B = 9 - A$ to get $B = 9 - 5 = 4$. Now we know that $A = 5$ and $B = 4$, such that $\frac{9x+2}{(x+3)(x-2)} = \frac{5}{x+3} + \frac{4}{x-2}$. The integral becomes:

$$\int \frac{9x + 2}{(x + 3)(x - 2)} dx = \int \frac{5}{x + 3} dx + \int \frac{4}{x - 2} dx = 5 \int \frac{dx}{x + 3} + 4 \int \frac{dx}{x - 2}$$

These integrals are natural logs. Recall from calculus that $\int \frac{dx}{x+a} = \ln(x + a) + c$.

$$5 \int \frac{dx}{x + 3} + 4 \int \frac{dx}{x - 2} = \boxed{5 \ln(x + 3) + 4 \ln(x - 2) + c}$$

Since the problem states that $x > 2$, we don't need to worry about the argument of the natural logarithm being negative (which would pose a domain problem).

Date: ________________ Name: ____________________________________

Problem 40

Directions: Perform the following derivative. Express your result in the simplest form possible.

$$\frac{d}{dx}\frac{1-e^{-2\tan x}}{1+e^{-2\tan x}}$$

❖You can find the solution on the following page.

Solution to Problem 40

Apply the quotient rule with $p = 1 - e^{-2\tan x}$ and $q = 1 + e^{-2\tan x}$.

$$\frac{d}{dx}\left(\frac{p}{q}\right) = \frac{q\frac{dp}{dx} - p\frac{dq}{dx}}{q^2}$$

$$= \frac{(1 + e^{-2\tan x})\frac{d}{dx}(1 - e^{-2\tan x}) - (1 - e^{-2\tan x})\frac{d}{dx}(1 + e^{-2\tan x})}{(1 + e^{-2\tan x})^2}$$

Apply the chain rule with $f = 1 - e^{-u}$, $g = 1 + e^{-u}$, and $u = 2\tan x$.

$$\frac{d}{dx}\left(\frac{p}{q}\right) = \frac{(1 + e^{-2\tan x})\frac{df}{du}\frac{du}{dx} - (1 - e^{-2\tan x})\frac{dg}{du}\frac{du}{dx}}{(1 + e^{-2\tan x})^2}$$

$$= \frac{(1 + e^{-2\tan x})\frac{d}{du}(1 - e^{-u})\frac{d}{dx}(2\tan x) - (1 - e^{-2\tan x})\frac{d}{du}(1 + e^{-u})\frac{d}{dx}(2\tan x)}{(1 + e^{-2\tan x})^2}$$

$$= \frac{(1 + e^{-2\tan x})(e^{-u})(2\sec^2 x) - (1 - e^{-2\tan x})(-e^{-u})(2\sec^2 x)}{(1 + e^{-2\tan x})^2}$$

$$= \frac{(1 + e^{-2\tan x})(e^{-u})(2\sec^2 x) + (1 - e^{-2\tan x})(e^{-u})(2\sec^2 x)}{(1 + e^{-2\tan x})^2}$$

$$= \frac{2\sec^2 x\, e^{-2\tan x}(1 + e^{-2\tan x}) + 2\sec^2 x\, e^{-2\tan x}(1 - e^{-2\tan x})}{(1 + e^{-2\tan x})^2}$$

$$= \frac{2\sec^2 x\, e^{-2\tan x}(1 + e^{-2\tan x} + 1 - e^{-2\tan x})}{(1 + e^{-2\tan x})^2} = \frac{2\sec^2 x\, e^{-2\tan x}(2)}{(1 + e^{-2\tan x})^2}$$

$$= \frac{4\sec^2 x\, e^{-2\tan x}}{(1 + e^{-2\tan x})^2} = \frac{4\sec^2 x\, e^{-2\tan x}}{(1 + e^{-2\tan x})^2}\left(\frac{e^{2\tan x}}{e^{2\tan x}}\right) = \frac{4\sec^2 x}{(1 + e^{-2\tan x})^2 e^{2\tan x}}$$

$$= \frac{4\sec^2 x}{(1 + e^{-2\tan x})(1 + e^{-2\tan x})e^{2\tan x}} = \frac{4\sec^2 x}{(1 + e^{-2\tan x})(1 + e^{-2\tan x})e^{\tan x}e^{\tan x}}$$

$$= \frac{4\sec^2 x}{[(1 + e^{-2\tan x})e^{\tan x}]^2} = \frac{4\sec^2 x}{(e^{\tan x} + e^{-2\tan x}e^{\tan x})^2} = \frac{\sec^2 x}{(e^{\tan x} + e^{-\tan x})^2}$$

$$= \boxed{\sec^2 x\,\mathrm{sech}^2(\tan x)}$$

Recall the hyperbolic function $\mathrm{sech}\, x = \frac{1}{\cosh x} = \frac{2}{e^x + e^{-x}}$, such that $\mathrm{sech}^2 x = \frac{4}{(e^x + e^{-x})^2}$. Note that $e^{2\tan x} = e^{\tan x}e^{\tan x}$ according to $x^m x^m = x^{2m}$. If you multiply $\frac{1 - e^{-2\tan x}}{1 + e^{-2\tan x}}$ by $\frac{e^{\tan x}}{e^{\tan x}}$, you get $\frac{e^{\tan x} - e^{-\tan x}}{e^{\tan x} + e^{-\tan x}} = \tanh(\tan x)$, for which $\frac{d}{dx}[\tanh(\tan x)] = \sec^2 x\,\mathrm{sech}^2(\tan x)$.

Date: ____________ Name: ______________________________

Problem 41

Directions: A system obeys the following equations, where a, b, and r are constants:

$$xy = (b - a)z$$
$$a\,dz = -x\,dy$$
$$r = \frac{b}{a}$$

Prove that xy^r equals a constant.

❖You can find the solution on the following page.

Solution to Problem 41

The problem is that the first equation, $xy = (b-a)z$, doesn't involve any differentials, whereas the second equation, $a\,dz = -x\,dy$, does. It would help if we could write the first equation in terms of differentials. How can we do that? The answer is to take an implicit derivative of both sides of the equation. On the left-hand side, apply the product rule to write $d(xy) = y\,dx + x\,dy$. On the right-hand side, we get $(b-a)dz$.

$$y\,dx + x\,dy = (b-a)dz$$

Solve for dz in the second equation: $dz = -\frac{x}{a}dy$. Plug this into the previous equation.

$$y\,dx + x\,dy = (b-a)\left(-\frac{x}{a}dy\right) = -\left(\frac{b-a}{a}\right)x\,dy$$

Combine like differentials: Add $\frac{b-a}{a}x\,dy$ to both sides and subtract $y\,dx$.

$$x\,dy + \left(\frac{b-a}{a}\right)x\,dy = -y\,dx$$

Factor out $x\,dy$ on the left-hand side.

$$\left(1 + \frac{b-a}{a}\right)x\,dy = -y\,dx \quad \to \quad \left(\frac{a}{a} + \frac{b-a}{a}\right)x\,dy = -y\,dx$$

$$\left(\frac{a+b-a}{a}\right)x\,dy = -y\,dx \quad \to \quad \left(\frac{b}{a}\right)x\,dy = -y\,dx$$

According to the problem, $\frac{b}{a} = r$.

$$rx\,dy = -y\,dx$$

Separate variables: Divide both sides of the equation by xy.

$$\frac{rdy}{y} = -\frac{dx}{x}$$

Now that we have separated variables, we may integrate both sides.

$$r\int\frac{dy}{y} = -\int\frac{dx}{x} \quad \to \quad r\ln(y) = -\ln(x) + c \to \quad r\ln(y) = -\ln(x) + \ln(d)$$

We chose to define the constant of integration in terms of a new constant: $c = \ln(d)$. Recall the rules $-\ln(x) = \ln\left(\frac{1}{x}\right)$, $r\ln(y) = \ln(y^r)$, and $\ln(pq) = \ln(p) + \ln(q)$.

$$\ln(y^r) = \ln\left(\frac{1}{x}\right) + \ln(d) = \ln\left(\frac{d}{x}\right)$$

Exponentiate both sides of the equation. Recall the rule $e^{\ln p} = p$.

$$e^{\ln(y^r)} = e^{\ln\left(\frac{d}{x}\right)} \quad \to \quad y^r = \frac{d}{x} \quad \to \quad \boxed{xy^r = d = \text{constant}}$$

Date: ______________ Name: ______________________________

Problem 42

Directions: Derive the formula for the volume of the right-circular cone shown below using a single integral (not by using a double or triple integral).

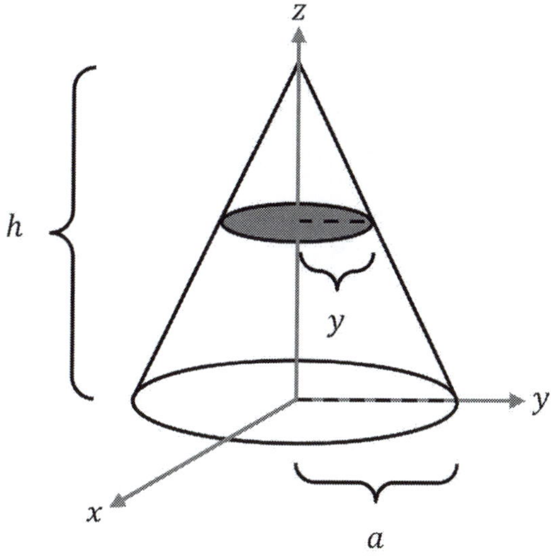

❖You can find the solution on the following page.

Solution to Problem 42

Consider the gray-colored disc with radius y shown in the figure on the previous page. This disc is very thin: Its thickness is dz. The area of this disc is $A = \pi y^2$ and its volume is $dV = \pi y^2 dz$. Now consider the straight line forming the right edge of the cone. The slope of this line is $-\frac{h}{a}$ and its z-intercept is h. The equation for this line is $z = -\frac{h}{a}y + h$. (Since z is on the vertical axis and y is on the horizontal axis, this line has the form $z = my + b$ instead of $y = mx + b$.) Solve for y in the equation for the line.

$$z = -\frac{h}{a}y + h \quad \to \quad z - h = -\frac{h}{a}y \quad \to \quad -\frac{a}{h}(z - h) = y$$

Substitute this equation for y into the equation for the volume of the thin disc.

$$dV = \pi y^2 dz = dV = \pi\left[-\frac{a}{h}(z - h)\right]^2 dz = \pi\left(-\frac{a}{h}\right)^2 (z - h)^2 dz = \frac{\pi a^2}{h^2}(z - h)^2 dz$$

Integrate over the height of the cone to get the total volume of the cone.

$$V = \int dV = \int_{z=0}^{h} \frac{\pi a^2}{h^2}(z - h)^2\, dz = \frac{\pi a^2}{h^2}\int_{z=0}^{h} (z - h)^2\, dz = \frac{\pi a^2}{h^2}\int_{z=0}^{h} (z^2 - 2zh + h^2)\, dz$$

$$= \frac{\pi a^2}{h^2}\left[\frac{z^3}{3} - z^2 h + h^2 z\right]_{z=0}^{h} = \frac{\pi a^2}{h^2}\left(\frac{h^3}{3} - h^3 + h^3\right) = \frac{\pi a^2}{h^2}\left(\frac{h^3}{3}\right) = \boxed{\frac{\pi a^2 h}{3}}$$

(In calculus, you learn how to solve problems with a similar method in the context of "volume of revolution.") You can also check the answer by looking up the standard formula for the volume of a right-circular cone.

Date: ____________________ Name: ____

Problem 43

Directions: Determine the arc length from $(0,0)$ to $\left(\frac{\pi}{4}, \ln\sqrt{2}\right)$ along the curve below.

$$y = \ln(\sec x)$$

❖You can find the solution on the following page.

Solution to Problem 43

Perform the arc length integral:

$$s = \int_{x=0}^{\pi/4} \sqrt{1 + \left(\frac{dy}{dx}\right)^2}\, dx$$

Plug in the equation given in the problem: $y = \ln(\sec x)$.

$$s = \int_{x=0}^{\pi/4} \sqrt{1 + \left[\frac{d}{dx}\ln(\sec x)\right]^2}\, dx$$

Apply the chain rule with $f = \ln u$ and $u = \sec x$:

$$\frac{d}{dx}\ln(\sec x) = \frac{df}{du}\frac{du}{dx} = \frac{d}{du}\ln u \frac{d}{dx}\sec x = \frac{1}{u}\sec x \tan x = \frac{\sec x \tan x}{\sec x} = \tan x$$

If you remembered that $\int \tan x\, dx = \ln|\sec x|$, it would have been much easier to see that $\frac{d}{dx}\ln(\sec x) = \tan x$. Substitute $\frac{d}{dx}\ln(\sec x) = \tan x$ into the integral.

$$s = \int_{x=0}^{\pi/4} \sqrt{1 + \tan^2 x}\, dx$$

Recall the trig identity $\tan^2 x + 1 = \sec^2 x$. Note that $\tan^2 x + 1 = 1 + \tan^2 x$.

$$s = \int_{x=0}^{\pi/4} \sqrt{\sec^2 x}\, dx = \int_{x=0}^{\pi/4} \sec x\, dx = [\ln|\sec x + \tan x|]_{x=0}^{\frac{\pi}{4}}$$

$$= \ln\left|\sec\frac{\pi}{4} + \tan\frac{\pi}{4}\right| - \ln|\sec 0 + \tan 0| = \ln\left|\sqrt{2} + 1\right| - \ln|1 + 0|$$

$$= \ln\left(\sqrt{2} + 1\right) - \ln 1 = \ln\left(\sqrt{2} + 1\right) - 0 = \boxed{\ln\left(\sqrt{2} + 1\right)} \approx \boxed{0.881}$$

Note that $\sec 0 = \frac{1}{\cos 0} = \frac{1}{1} = 1$, $\tan 0 = 0$, $\sec\frac{\pi}{4} = \sec 45° = \frac{1}{\cos 45°} = \frac{1}{\sqrt{2}/2} = \frac{2}{\sqrt{2}} = \sqrt{2}$ (because $\sqrt{2}\sqrt{2} = 2$), $\tan\frac{\pi}{4} = \tan 45° = 1$, and $\ln 1 = 0$.

Date: ________________ Name: ____________________________________

Problem 44

Directions: Perform the following integral.

$$\int_{\theta=0}^{\pi/6} \sec^3 \theta \, d\theta$$

❖You can find the solution on the following page.

Solution to Problem 44

The 'trick' to this integral is to integrate by parts with $u = \sec\theta$ and $dv = \sec^2\theta\, d\theta$. With this choice, $du = \sec\theta\tan\theta\, d\theta$ (because $\frac{d}{d\theta}\sec\theta = \sec\theta\tan\theta$) and $v = \tan\theta$ (because $\frac{d}{d\theta}\tan\theta = \sec^2\theta$). Recall the formula $\int_i^f u\, dv = [uv]_i^f - \int_i^f v\, du$. Note that $\sec^3\theta\, d\theta = (\sec\theta)(\sec^2\theta\, d\theta) = u\, dv$.

$$\int_{\theta=0}^{\pi/6} \sec^3\theta\, d\theta = [\sec\theta\tan\theta]_{\theta=0}^{\frac{\pi}{6}} - \int_{\theta=0}^{\pi/6} (\tan\theta)\,(\sec\theta\tan\theta\, d\theta)$$

$$\int_{\theta=0}^{\pi/6} \sec^3\theta\, d\theta = [\sec\theta\tan\theta]_{\theta=0}^{\frac{\pi}{6}} - \int_{\theta=0}^{\pi/6} \sec\theta\tan^2\theta\, d\theta$$

Apply the trig identity $\tan^2\theta + 1 = \sec^2\theta$, which equates to $\tan^2\theta = \sec^2\theta - 1$.

$$\int_{\theta=0}^{\pi/6} \sec^3\theta\, d\theta = [\sec\theta\tan\theta]_{\theta=0}^{\frac{\pi}{6}} - \int_{\theta=0}^{\pi/6} \sec\theta\,(\sec^2\theta - 1)\, d\theta$$

$$\int_{\theta=0}^{\pi/6} \sec^3\theta\, d\theta = [\sec\theta\tan\theta]_{\theta=0}^{\frac{\pi}{6}} - \int_{\theta=0}^{\frac{\pi}{6}} \sec^3\theta\, d\theta + \int_{\theta=0}^{\pi/6} \sec\theta\, d\theta$$

Add $\int_{\theta=0}^{\frac{\pi}{6}} \sec^3\theta\, d\theta$ to both sides of the equation. Then divide both sides by 2. Note that $\int \sec x\, dx = \ln|\sec x + \tan x|$.

$$2\int_{\theta=0}^{\pi/6} \sec^3\theta\, d\theta = [\sec\theta\tan\theta]_{\theta=0}^{\frac{\pi}{6}} + \int_{\theta=0}^{\pi/6} \sec\theta\, d\theta$$

$$\int_{\theta=0}^{\pi/6} \sec^3\theta\, d\theta = \frac{1}{2}[\sec\theta\tan\theta]_{\theta=0}^{\frac{\pi}{6}} + \frac{1}{2}\int_{\theta=0}^{\pi/6} \sec\theta\, d\theta$$

$$= \frac{1}{2}[\sec\theta\tan\theta]_{\theta=0}^{\frac{\pi}{6}} + \frac{1}{2}[\ln|\sec\theta + \tan\theta|]_{\theta=0}^{\frac{\pi}{6}}$$

$$= \frac{1}{2}\left(\sec\frac{\pi}{6}\tan\frac{\pi}{6} - \sec 0\tan 0\right) + \frac{1}{2}\left(\ln\left|\sec\frac{\pi}{6} + \tan\frac{\pi}{6}\right| - \ln|\sec 0 + \tan 0|\right)$$

$$= \frac{1}{2}\left[\frac{2}{\sqrt{3}}\frac{1}{\sqrt{3}} - (1)(0)\right] + \frac{1}{2}\left(\ln\left|\frac{2}{\sqrt{3}} + \frac{1}{\sqrt{3}}\right| - \ln|1+0|\right)$$

$$= \frac{1}{2}\left(\frac{2}{3} - 0\right) + \frac{1}{2}\left(\ln\left|\frac{3}{\sqrt{3}}\right| - \ln|1|\right) = \frac{1}{2}\left(\frac{2}{3}\right) + \frac{1}{2}(\ln\sqrt{3} - 0) = \boxed{\frac{1}{3} + \frac{\ln\sqrt{3}}{2}} \approx \boxed{0.608}$$

Date: ________________   Name: ______________________________

Problem 45

Directions: A function $g(t)$ is graphed below.

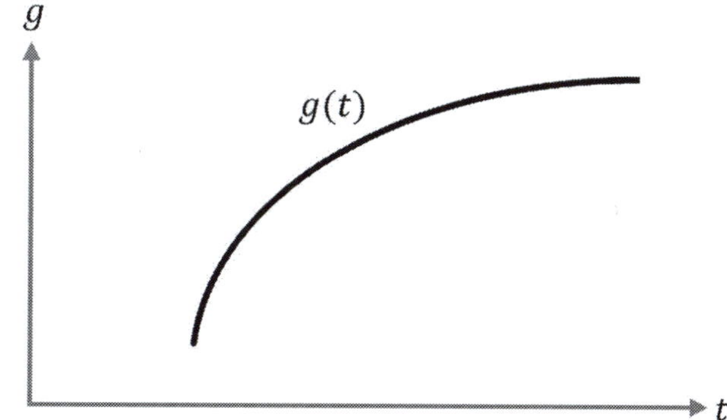

(A) Sketch a graph of $\frac{dg}{dt}$ as a function of t.

(B) Sketch a graph of $\int g\, dt$ as a function of t.

❖You can find the solution on the following page.

Solution to Problem 45

(A) To find $\frac{dg}{dt}$, take a derivative of g with respect to t. How do you find a derivative from a graph? The derivative represents the slope of the tangent line. For the given graph, the tangent line starts out steep and drops to zero (since it is horizontal near the end). Thus, the derivative starts out positive (where g has a steep slope) and drops toward zero (where g is nearly horizontal).

Note: The equations in the margins aren't needed to solve the problem. They are only given in case you are skeptical about the solution, in which case you can plot the given equations on a computer to check our graphs.

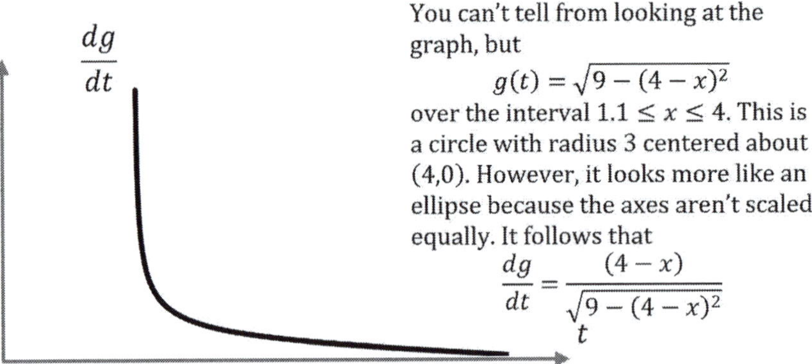

You can't tell from looking at the graph, but

$$g(t) = \sqrt{9-(4-x)^2}$$

over the interval $1.1 \leq x \leq 4$. This is a circle with radius 3 centered about (4,0). However, it looks more like an ellipse because the axes aren't scaled equally. It follows that

$$\frac{dg}{dt} = \frac{(4-x)}{\sqrt{9-(4-x)^2}}$$

(B) Although the integral $\int g\,dt$ represents the area under the given curve, it is easier to sketch $\int g\,dt$ by thinking of it as the antiderivative of g. To find the derivative (as we did in Part A), the slopes of the tangent lines give the values of the derivative. Therefore, to find the antiderivative, the values of g must give the slopes of $\int g\,dt$. It's the opposite of what we did in Part A. For the given graph, the values start out small (a little above zero) and grow; the values grow faster in the beginning, and grow at a more constant rate toward the end (approaching an upper limit). Thus, the antiderivative starts out with a small positive slope (where g has a small positive value) and becomes steeper (since g grows larger), reaching a maximum positive slope (the maximum value of g). You may shift the entire graph up or down (corresponding to an arbitrary constant of integration).

You can't get this by looking at the graph, but since $g(t) = \sqrt{9-(4-x)^2}$, it follows that $\int g\,dt$ equals

$$-\frac{9}{2}\sin^{-1}\left(\frac{4-x}{3}\right) - \frac{9}{4}\sin\left[2\sin^{-1}\left(\frac{4-x}{3}\right)\right]$$

Make the substitutions $4-x = 3\sin\theta$ and $dx = -3\cos\theta\,d\theta$, and apply the identity $\cos^2\theta = \frac{1+\cos 2\theta}{2}$.

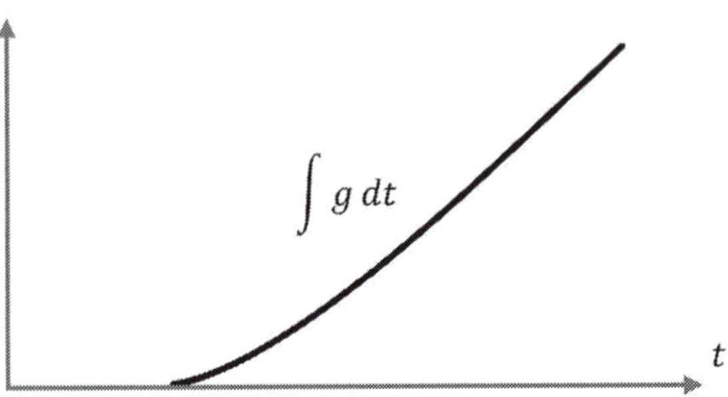

Date: ____________________ Name: ____

Problem 46

Directions: As illustrated below, a bowl in the shape of a perfect hemisphere is partially filled with water. The height from the <u>bottom</u> of the bowl to the water level is h. The radius of the bowl is a. Perform a triple integral in order to derive an equation for the volume of the region filled with water.

❖You can find the solution on the following page.

Solution to Problem 46

If the water had been filled to the top of the hemisphere, then it would have been convenient to work with spherical coordinates, as all of the limits of integration would have been constant. However, for this problem, one limit of integration would be less straightforward to write down. Why? Because one limit of integration corresponds to the flat plane of the water level, and since it's not as easy to write down the equation of that plane using spherical coordinates. This problem is more straightforward if you use cylindrical coordinates instead, where r is the distance from the z-axis (not the distance from the origin) and z is the vertical distance from the xy plane. In cylindrical coordinates, the volume element is $dV = r dr d\theta dz$ (that 'extra' r gives units of m^3). Note that z varies from $a - h$ to a, and that for a given value of z, the variable r varies from 0 to the equation for the circle, $r^2 + z^2 = a^2$. Solve for r to get $\sqrt{a^2 - z^2}$. We must integrate over r before z because it has a variable limit. The angular integral simply equals $\int_{\theta=0}^{2\pi} d\theta = [\theta]_{\theta=0}^{2\pi} = 2\pi - 0 = 2\pi$. (It may help to review Problem 42.)

$$V = \int_{r=0}^{\sqrt{a^2-z^2}} \int_{\theta=0}^{2\pi} \int_{z=a-h}^{a} r\, dr\, d\theta\, dz = 2\pi \int_{z=a-h}^{a} \left(\int_{r=0}^{\sqrt{a^2-z^2}} r\, dr \right) dz = 2\pi \int_{z=a-h}^{a} \left[\frac{r^2}{2} \right]_{r=0}^{\sqrt{a^2-z^2}} dz$$

$$= \pi \int_{z=a-h}^{a} [r^2]_{r=0}^{\sqrt{a^2-z^2}} dz = \pi \int_{z=a-h}^{a} \left[\left(\sqrt{a^2 - z^2}\right)^2 - 0^2 \right] dz = \pi \int_{z=a-h}^{a} (a^2 - z^2)\, dz$$

$$= \pi [a^2 z]_{z=a-h}^{a} - \pi \left[\frac{z^3}{3} \right]_{z=a-h}^{a} = \pi a^2 [a - (a - h)] - \pi \left[\frac{a^3}{3} - \frac{(a-h)^3}{3} \right]$$

$$= \pi a^2 (a - a + h) - \pi \frac{a^3}{3} + \pi \frac{(a-h)^3}{3} = \pi a^2 h - \pi \frac{a^3}{3} + \pi \frac{(a-h)^3}{3}$$

$$= \pi a^2 h - \pi \frac{a^3}{3} + \frac{\pi (a^3 - 3a^2 h + 3ah^2 - h^3)}{3} = \boxed{\pi a h^2 - \pi \frac{h^3}{3}} = \boxed{\pi h^2 \left(a - \frac{h}{3} \right)}$$

Note: Some books and online articles have a similar problem where they define h differently than we have. Of course, you get a different answer that way. Check the extreme cases to see that our answer is plausible: When $h = a$, the hemisphere is full and the volume is half of a sphere, $\frac{2\pi a^3}{3}$. When $h = 0$, it is empty and the volume is 0.

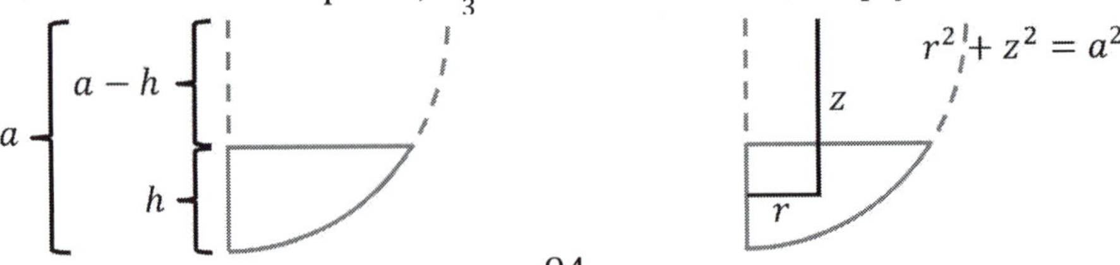

Date: ____________ Name: ______________________________

Problem 47

Directions: A projectile moves according to the parametric equations below.

$$x = 30t \quad , \quad y = 40t - 5t^2$$

(A) Find the slope of the tangent line when $t = 5$.

(B) At what time is the path of the projectile temporarily horizontal?

(C) Determine $\frac{d^2y}{dx^2}$.

❖You can find the solution on the following page.

Solution to Problem 47

(A) The derivative $\frac{dy}{dx}$ gives the slope of the line tangent to the projectile's path. To take a derivative of parametric equations, apply the chain rule. According to the chain rule, $\frac{dy}{dt} = \frac{dy}{dx}\frac{dx}{dt}$. Divide both sides by $\frac{dx}{dt}$ in order to solve for $\frac{dy}{dx}$:

$$\frac{dy}{dx} = \frac{dy/dt}{dx/dt} = \frac{\frac{d}{dt}(40t - 5t^2)}{\frac{d}{dt}(30t)} = \frac{40 - 10t}{30} = \frac{4 - t}{3}$$

In the last step, we divided the numerator and denominator both by 10. Evaluate the derivative at $t = 5$ in order to determine the slope at the specified time.

$$\left.\frac{dy}{dx}\right|_{t=5} = \frac{4 - 5}{3} = \frac{-1}{3} = \boxed{-\frac{1}{3}} \approx \boxed{-0.333}$$

The negative sign indicates that the projectile is heading downward at this time.

(B) The path is temporarily horizontal when the slope of the tangent line is zero. We found the slope of the tangent in part A:

$$\frac{dy}{dx} = \frac{4 - t}{3}$$

Set the slope equal to zero and solve for time. Multiply both sides by 3.

$$0 = \frac{4 - t}{3} \quad \rightarrow \quad 0 = 4 - t \quad \rightarrow \quad t = \boxed{4}$$

(C) We found $\frac{dy}{dx}$ in part A. Take a second derivative using the same method. It helps to define another symbol: $u = \frac{dy}{dx}$. In part A, we found that $u = \frac{4-t}{3}$. Recall that we were given $x = 30t$ in the problem.

$$\frac{d^2y}{dx^2} = \frac{d}{dx}\frac{dy}{dx} = \frac{du}{dx} = \frac{du/dt}{dx/dt} = \frac{\frac{d}{dt}\left(\frac{4 - t}{3}\right)}{\frac{d}{dt}(30t)} = \frac{\frac{d}{dt}\frac{4}{3} - \frac{d}{dt}\frac{t}{3}}{\frac{d}{dt}(30t)} = \frac{0 - \frac{1}{3}}{30} = -\frac{1/3}{30}$$

$$\frac{d^2y}{dx^2} = -\frac{1}{3} \div 30 = -\frac{1}{3} \times \frac{1}{30} = \boxed{-\frac{1}{90}} \approx \boxed{-0.011}$$

By the way, this second derivative doesn't represent acceleration, of course, since the derivative isn't with respect to time. The components of the acceleration are instead represented by $\frac{d^2x}{dt^2}$ and $\frac{d^2y}{dt^2}$. They are related to $\frac{d^2y}{dx^2}$ by $\frac{d^2y}{dx^2} = \frac{\frac{dx}{dt}\left(\frac{d^2y}{dt^2}\right) - \frac{dy}{dt}\left(\frac{d^2x}{dt^2}\right)}{\left(\frac{dx}{dt}\right)^3}$.

Date: ______________ Name: ______________________________

Problem 48

Directions: Carry out a Taylor series expansion of the following function about $x = 0$ for $-a < x < a$, keeping the first three terms of the expansion.

$$f(x) = \frac{1}{\sqrt{x^2 + a^2}}$$

❖You can find the solution on the following page.

Solution to Problem 48

Apply the rules $\sqrt{y} = y^{1/2}$ and $y^{-n} = \frac{1}{y^n}$ to rewrite the function as:

$$f(x) = \frac{1}{\sqrt{x^2 + a^2}} = \frac{1}{(x^2 + a^2)^{1/2}} = (x^2 + a^2)^{-1/2}$$

The trick is to write this in the form of the standard binomial expansion by making the substitution $u = \frac{x^2}{a^2}$, which can also be expressed as $x^2 = ua^2$.

$$f(x) = (ua^2 + a^2)^{-1/2}$$

Factor out a^2.

$$f(x) = [a^2(u + 1)]^{-1/2}$$

Apply the rule $(cy)^n = c^n y^n$. Note that $a^{-1} = \frac{1}{a}$.

$$f(x) = (a^2)^{-1/2}(u + 1)^{-1/2} = a^{-1}(u + 1)^{-1/2} = \frac{1}{a}(u + 1)^{-1/2}$$

The function $(1 + u)^{-1/2}$ is the standard binomial function $(1 + u)^p$ with $p = -\frac{1}{2}$, for which a Taylor series expansion gives:

$$(1 + u)^{-1/2} = (1 + u)^{-1/2}\Big|_{u=0} + \frac{d}{du}(1 + u)^{-1/2}\Big|_{u=0} u + \frac{1}{2!}\frac{d^2}{du^2}(1 + u)^{-1/2}\Big|_{u=0} u^2 + \cdots$$

$$= (1 + 0)^{-1/2} + \left(-\frac{1}{2}\right)(1 + u)^{-3/2}\Big|_{u=0} u + \frac{1}{2}\left(-\frac{1}{2}\right)\left(-\frac{3}{2}\right)(1 + u)^{-5/2}\Big|_{u=0} u^2 + \cdots$$

$$= (1)^{-1/2} - \frac{1}{2}(1 + 0)^{-3/2}u + \frac{3}{8}(1 + 0)^{-5/2}u^2 + \cdots$$

$$= 1 - \frac{u}{2}(1)^{-3/2} + \frac{3u^2}{8}(1)^{-5/2} + \cdots = 1 - \frac{u}{2} + \frac{3u^2}{8} + \cdots$$

Since $f(x) = \frac{1}{a}(1 + u)^{-1/2}$ in our problem (see above), we need to multiply by $\frac{1}{a}$:

$$f(x) = \frac{1}{a}(1 + u)^{-1/2} = \frac{1}{a} - \frac{u}{2a} + \frac{3u^2}{8a} + \cdots$$

Substitute $u = \frac{x^2}{a^2}$ into the previous expansion. Note that $\left(\frac{x^2}{a^2}\right)^2 = \frac{x^4}{a^4}$.

$$f(x) = \frac{1}{a} - \frac{1}{2a}\frac{x^2}{a^2} + \frac{3}{8a}\left(\frac{x^2}{a^2}\right)^2 + \cdots = \boxed{\frac{1}{a} - \frac{x^2}{2a^3} + \frac{3x^4}{8a^5} + \cdots}$$

The binomial expansion, $(1 + u)^p$, converges for $-1 < u < 1$, which corresponds to $-a < x < a$. (Since $u = \frac{x^2}{a^2}$ in this problem, we actually have $0 \leq u < 1$.)

Date: ______________ Name: ______________________________

Problem 49

Directions: Perform the following derivative. Factor your answer.

$$\frac{d}{dx}[(6-x)^9(3x^2+4)^7(5x-2)^8]$$

❖You can find the solution on the following page.

Solution to Problem 49

Apply the product rule with $f = (6-x)^9$ and $g = (3x^2+4)^7(5x-2)^8$

$$\frac{d}{dx}[(6-x)^9(3x^2+4)^7(5x-2)^8] = \frac{d}{dx}(fg) = g\frac{df}{dx} + f\frac{dg}{dx}$$

$$= (3x^2+4)^7(5x-2)^8\frac{d}{dx}(6-x)^9 + (6-x)^9\frac{d}{dx}[(3x^2+4)^7(5x-2)^8]$$

$$= (3x^2+4)^7(5x-2)^8[9(-1)(6-x)^8] + (6-x)^9\frac{d}{dx}[(3x^2+4)^7(5x-2)^8]$$

$$= -9(3x^2+4)^7(5x-2)^8(6-x)^8 + (6-x)^9\frac{d}{dx}[(3x^2+4)^7(5x-2)^8]$$

Note that $\frac{d}{dx}(6-x)^9 = \frac{dh}{dx} = \frac{dh}{du}\frac{du}{dx} = \left(\frac{d}{du}u^9\right)\left[\frac{d}{dx}(6-x)\right] = 9u^8(-1) = -9(6-x)^8$ using the chain rule with $h = u^9$ and $u = 6-x$. Apply the product rule a second time with $p = (3x^2+4)^7$ and $q = (5x-2)^8$. The chain rule gives $\frac{d}{dx}(3x^2+4)^7 = 7(6x)(3x^2+4)^6$ and $\frac{d}{dx}(5x-2)^8 = 8(5)(5x-2)^7$.

$$\frac{d}{dx}[(3x^2+4)^7(5x-2)^8] = (5x-2)^8\frac{d}{dx}(3x^2+4)^7 + (3x^2+4)^7\frac{d}{dx}(5x-2)^8$$

$$= (5x-2)^8[7(6x)(3x^2+4)^6] + (3x^2+4)^7[8(5)(5x-2)^7]$$

$$= 42x(5x-2)^8(3x^2+4)^6 + 40(3x^2+4)^7(5x-2)^7$$

Substitute the previous equation into the equation from the first product rule.

$$\frac{d}{dx}(fg) = -9(3x^2+4)^7(5x-2)^8(6-x)^8 + (6-x)^9\frac{d}{dx}[(3x^2+4)^7(5x-2)^8]$$

$$= -9(3x^2+4)^7(5x-2)^8(6-x)^8$$
$$+ (6-x)^9[42x(5x-2)^8(3x^2+4)^6 + 40(3x^2+4)^7(5x-2)^7]$$

$$= -9(3x^2+4)^7(5x-2)^8(6-x)^8 + 42x(6-x)^9(5x-2)^8(3x^2+4)^6$$
$$+ 40(6-x)^9(3x^2+4)^7(5x-2)^7$$

The problems says to "factor" the answer. Note that $(3x^2+4)^6(5x-2)^7(6-x)^8$ is common to every term. We will factor out $(3x^2+4)^6(5x-2)^7(6-x)^8$.

$$d(fg) = (3x^2+4)^6(5x-2)^7(6-x)^8[-9(3x^2+4)(5x-2) + 42x(6-x)(5x-2)$$
$$+ 40(6-x)(3x^2+4)]$$

$$= (3x^2+4)^6(5x-2)^7(6-x)^8[-9(15x^3-6x^2+20x-8) + 42x(30x-12-5x^2+2x)$$
$$+ 40(18x^2+24-3x^3-4x)]$$

$$= (3x^2+4)^6(5x-2)^7(6-x)^8(-135x^3+54x^2-180x+72+1260x^2-504x-210x^3$$
$$+ 84x^2+720x^2+960-120x^3-160x)$$

$$= \boxed{(3x^2+4)^6(5x-2)^7(6-x)^8(-465x^3+2118x^2-844x+1032)}$$

Date: ________________ Name: ______________________________

Problem 50

Directions: Show that

$$\int_{x=0}^{\infty} e^{-ax^2}\,dx = \frac{1}{2}\sqrt{\frac{\pi}{a}}$$

Hint: Call this integral H and show that $H^2 = \frac{\pi}{4a}$. Note that H^2 involves a double integral. Transform this double integral to 2D polar coordinates (r and θ).

Note: This integral is from 0 to ∞. Some textbooks and online articles instead show a similar integral from $-\infty$ to ∞. In that case, the answer would be $\sqrt{\frac{\pi}{a}}$ instead of $\frac{1}{2}\sqrt{\frac{\pi}{a}}$.

❖You can find the solution on the following page.

Solution to Problem 50

The trick is to square the integral, write it as a double integral, and transform to 2D polar coordinates:

$$H^2 = \int_{x=0}^{\infty} e^{-ax^2}\,dx \int_{y=0}^{\infty} e^{-ay^2}\,dy = \int_{x=0}^{\infty}\int_{y=0}^{\infty} e^{-ax^2}e^{-ay^2}\,dxdy$$

Note that $e^{-ax^2}e^{-ay^2} = e^{-ax^2-ay^2} = e^{-a(x^2+y^2)}$ according to the rule $x^m x^n = x^{m+n}$.

$$H^2 = \int_{x=0}^{\infty}\int_{y=0}^{\infty} e^{-a(x^2+y^2)}\,dxdy$$

In 2D polar coordinates, the differential area element is $dA = dxdy = rdrd\theta$ (it may help to review the solution to Problem 31). The Cartesian coordinates are related to polar coordinates by $x = r\cos\theta$ and $y = r\sin\theta$, which shows that $x^2 + y^2 = r^2$ (since $\sin^2\theta + \cos^2\theta = 1$). The limits of integration, $0 \le x < \infty$ and $0 \le y < \infty$, correspond to Quadrant I in the xy plane. In polar coordinates, this corresponds to $0 \le r < \infty$ and $0 \le \theta \le \frac{\pi}{2}$. When we integrate over θ, we treat the independent variable r as if it were a constant. The angular integration equals $\frac{\pi}{2}$.

$$H^2 = \int_{r=0}^{\infty}\int_{\theta=0}^{\pi/2} e^{-ar^2}\,rdrd\theta = \int_{r=0}^{\infty} e^{-ar^2} r\,dr \int_{\theta=0}^{\pi/2} d\theta = \frac{\pi}{2}\int_{r=0}^{\infty} e^{-ar^2} r\,dr$$

Make the substitution $u = r^2$, such that $du = 2rdr$ (a derivative of r^2 with respect to r equals $2r$). Divide both sides of $du = 2rdr$ by 2 to see that $\frac{du}{2} = rdr$. The limits of integration are now $0 \le u < \infty$. Note that $\int e^{-au}\,du = \frac{e^{-au}}{-a}$.

$$H^2 = \frac{\pi}{2}\int_{r=0}^{\infty} e^{-au}\frac{du}{2} = \frac{\pi}{4}\int_{r=0}^{\infty} e^{-au}\,du = \frac{\pi}{4}\left[\frac{e^{-au}}{-a}\right]_{u=0}^{\infty} = -\frac{\pi}{4a}\left[e^{-au}\right]_{u=0}^{\infty}$$

$$H^2 = -\frac{\pi}{4a}\left[\left(\lim_{u\to\infty} e^{-au}\right) - e^0\right] = -\frac{\pi}{4a}(0-1) = -\frac{\pi}{4a}(-1) = \frac{\pi}{4a}$$

Note that $e^{-au} = \frac{1}{e^{au}}$ approaches zero as u grows to infinity. Also note that $e^0 = 1$. Squareroot both sides of the equation.

$$H = \sqrt{\frac{\pi}{4a}} = \boxed{\frac{1}{2}\sqrt{\frac{\pi}{a}}}$$

WAS THIS BOOK HELPFUL?

A great deal of effort and thought was put into this book, such as:

- Breaking down the solutions to help make the math easier to understand.
- Careful selection of problems for their instructional value.
- Coming up with a good variety of ways to offer a challenge.
- Multiple stages of proofreading, editing, and formatting.
- Beta testers provided valuable feedback.

If you appreciate the effort that went into making this book possible, there is a simple way that you could show it:

Please take a moment to post an honest review.

For example, you can review this book at Amazon.com or Barnes & Noble's website at BN.com.

Even a short review can be helpful and will be much appreciated. If you're not sure what to write, following are a few ideas, though it's best to describe what's important to you.

- Did you enjoy the selection of problems?
- Were you able to understand the solutions and explanations?
- Do you appreciate the handy formulas on the back cover of the print edition?
- How much did you learn from reading and using this workbook?
- Would you recommend this book to others? If so, why?

Do you believe that you found a mistake? Please email the author, Chris McMullen, at greekphysics@yahoo.com to ask about it. One of two things will happen:

- You might discover that it wasn't a mistake after all and learn why.
- You might be right, in which case the author will be grateful and future readers will benefit from the correction. Everyone is human.

ABOUT THE AUTHOR

Dr. Chris McMullen has over 20 years of experience teaching university physics in California, Oklahoma, Pennsylvania, and Louisiana. Dr. McMullen is also an author of math and science workbooks. Whether in the classroom or as a writer, Dr. McMullen loves sharing knowledge and the art of motivating and engaging students.

The author earned his Ph.D. in phenomenological high-energy physics (particle physics) from Oklahoma State University in 2002. Originally from California, Chris McMullen earned his Master's degree from California State University, Northridge, where his thesis was in the field of electron spin resonance.

As a physics teacher, Dr. McMullen observed that many students lack fluency in fundamental math skills. In an effort to help students of all ages and levels master basic math skills, he published a series of math workbooks on arithmetic, fractions, long division, algebra, trigonometry, and calculus entitled *Improve Your Math Fluency*. Dr. McMullen has also published a variety of science books, including introductions to basic astronomy and chemistry concepts in addition to physics workbooks.

Author, Chris McMullen, Ph.D.

Essential

CALCULUS

Skills Practice Workbook

with Full Solutions

$$\frac{d}{dx}\tan(5x)$$

$$\int \sqrt{1 - x^2}\, dx$$

Chris McMullen, Ph.D.

50 CHALLENGING ALGEBRA PROBLEMS

$$3x - 2y$$

$$9x^2 - 12xy + 4y^2$$

$$27x^3 - 54x^2y + 36xy^2 - 8y^3$$

FULLY SOLVED

Chris McMullen, Ph.D.

Essential Calculus-based PHYSICS

Study Guide Workbook

Volume 1: The Laws of Motion

$$y_{cm} = \frac{1}{m}\int y\,dm$$

$$m = \int dm = \int \sigma\,dA = \frac{\sigma\pi R^2}{2}$$

$$y_{cm} = \frac{\sigma}{m}\int_{r=0}^{R}\int_{\theta=0}^{\pi}(r\sin\theta)\,r\,dr\,d\theta$$

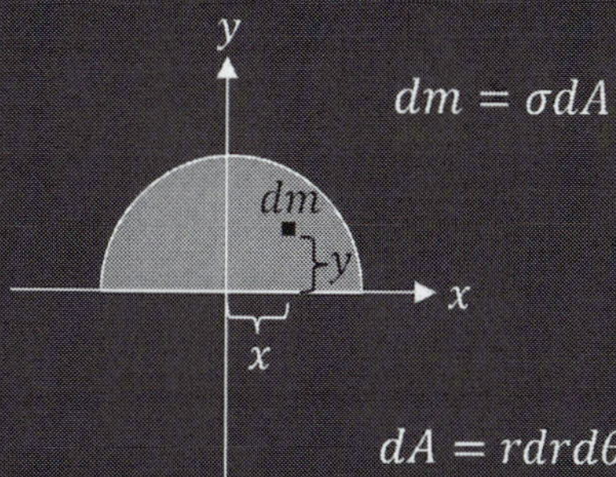

$$dm = \sigma dA$$

$$y_{cm} = \frac{\sigma}{m}\int_{r=0}^{R} r^2[-\cos\pi - (-\cos 0)]\,dr$$

$$y_{cm} = \frac{2\sigma}{m}\int_{r=0}^{R} r^2\,dr = \frac{2\sigma R^3}{3m}$$

$$dA = rdrd\theta$$

$$y_{cm} = \frac{2\sigma R^3}{3}\frac{2}{\sigma\pi R^2} = \frac{4R}{3\pi}$$

$$y = r\sin\theta$$

Chris McMullen, Ph.D.

SCIENCE

Dr. McMullen has published a variety of **science** books, including:

- Basic astronomy concepts
- Basic chemistry concepts
- Balancing chemical reactions
- Calculus-based physics textbooks
- Calculus-based physics workbooks
- Calculus-based physics examples
- Trig-based physics workbooks
- Trig-based physics examples
- Creative physics problems

www.monkeyphysicsblog.wordpress.com

ALGEBRA

For students who need to improve their algebra skills:

- Isolating the unknown
- Quadratic equations
- Factoring
- Cross multiplying
- Systems of equations
- Straight line graphs

www.improveyourmathfluency.com

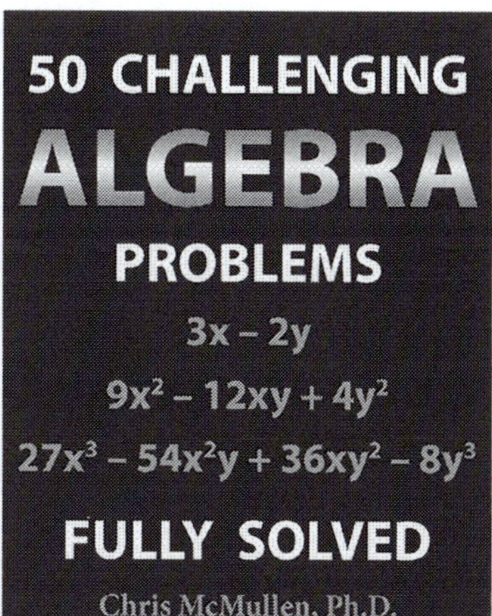

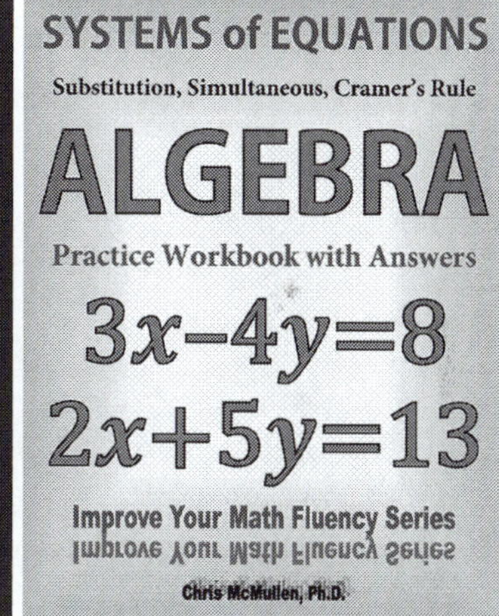

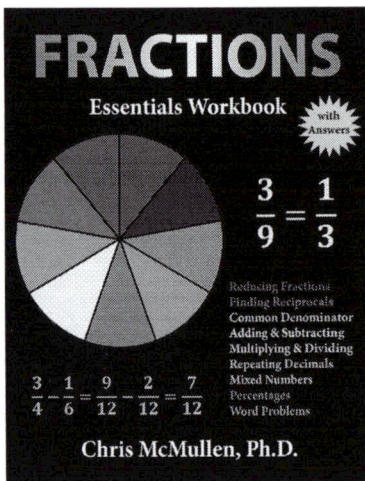

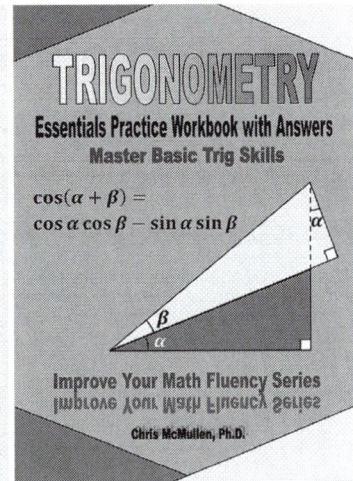

PUZZLES

The author of this book, Chris McMullen, enjoys solving puzzles. His favorite puzzle is Kakuro (kind of like a cross between crossword puzzles and Sudoku). He once taught a three-week summer course on puzzles. If you enjoy mathematical pattern puzzles, you might appreciate:

300+ Mathematical Pattern Puzzles

Number Pattern Recognition & Reasoning

- Pattern recognition
- Visual discrimination
- Analytical skills
- Logic and reasoning
- Analogies
- Mathematics

THE FOURTH DIMENSION

Are you curious about a possible fourth dimension of space?

- Explore the world of hypercubes and hyperspheres.
- Imagine living in a two-dimensional world.
- Try to understand the fourth dimension by analogy.
- Several illustrations help to try to visualize a fourth dimension of space.
- Investigate hypercube patterns.
- What would it be like to be a four-dimensional being living in a four-dimensional world?
- Learn about the physics of a possible four-dimensional universe.

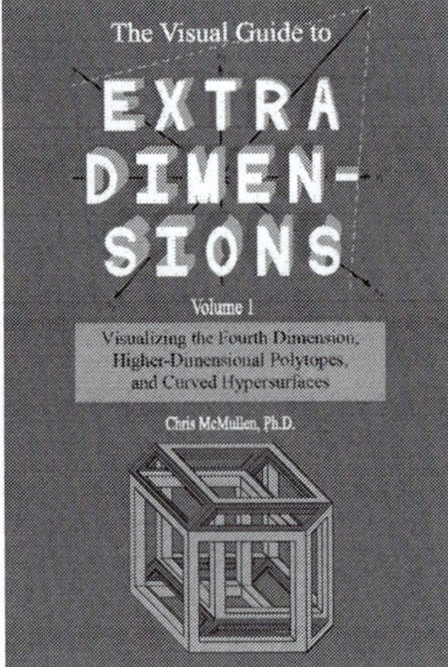

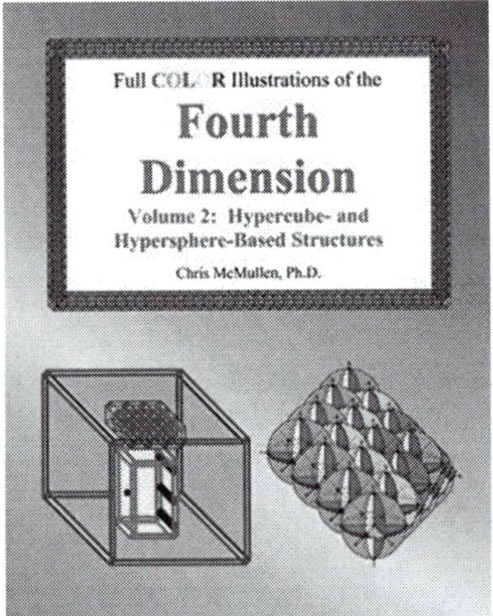

Made in the USA
Middletown, DE
03 January 2025